GREAT MEN OF MEDICINE

GREAT MEN OF MEDICINE

RUTH FOX HUME

ILLUSTRATED BY
Robert Frankenberg

RANDOM HOUSE – NEW YORK

FOR PAUL RUSSELL HUME, the scientific member of the quartet

CONTENTS

1

ANDREAS VESALIUS

———————— 1514 – 1564 ————————

The Founding
of Modern Medicine

Jacobus Sylvius, who was said to be the greatest teacher of medicine in all Europe, was a surly little man with a red nose and a bad temper. As he climbed to the elevated platform in the middle of the lecture hall to begin his first class of the year 1533, he said fretfully, "Two of you have not paid all your fees. If they are not paid by tomorrow there will be no class for anyone!" He coughed a few times to soothe his ruffled feelings and then began to lecture.

In the first row of benches there sat a young Belgian student who had come to Paris for the express purpose of studying with this man Sylvius. For years he had dreamed of the day when he, Andreas Vesalius, the apothecary's son, would be sitting in a lecture hall of the great University of Paris, listening to the famous teacher. And here he was. Here too, alas, was Jacobus Sylvius! So far, Jacobus Sylvius was a great disappointment.

Sylvius held up a large, well-worn book. "This divinely inspired volume, young gentlemen," he said, "is the *De Usu Partium*—On the Use of the Parts—by Galen. From it you will learn your art. Learn well from this book, young scholars, for I tell you that progress beyond Galen is impossible! He has said all that there is to be said about the human body." Then he opened the book and began to read from it in a low, monotonous voice. The class took notes at a furious pace, fearful of missing a single word. Very few students four hundred years ago could afford to own anything as rare and expensive as a book.

Vesalius, too, began copying down the words of Galen, although it occurred to the brilliant young man that someone must have learned *something* new about the human body in thirteen hundred years. Neither he nor anyone else in Paris, however, was prepared to argue with Galen.

Galen, the Greek physician of the wise Roman emperor, Marcus Aurelius, was truly a mighty man, as powerful in the year 1533 as he had been thirteen centuries earlier. For the idea had become firmly fixed in most people's minds that the ancient

Greek and Roman writers had somehow or other known all there was to know about medicine and science. The influence of Galen's writings was so strong that it was considered irreverent to dispute a word of them.

The anatomy course dragged on as it had begun. Sylvius read from the book, and the students copied down the words of Galen. Occasionally a dissection was made on the body of a dog or a pig. If any part of the animal's body differed from the description of the same part in the book, Sylvius informed the class that the dog or pig was "wrong" and had no business contradicting Galen.

Dissections on the human body were rarer still. The practice was frowned upon and was seldom permitted. And when the city officials did, on occasion, hand over the body of an executed criminal to the University professors, the valuable material was wasted.

Neither Jacobus Sylvius nor John Guinther, Vesalius' other professor of anatomy, enjoyed or excelled in dissection. "I would not mind having as many cuts inflicted on me," Vesalius later wrote about Guinther, "as I have seen him make either on man or other brute—except at the banqueting table."

Such activity as cutting up dead bodies was far beneath the dignity of a professor. Ignorant barber-surgeons, the cheaper the better, were called in to do the job. From his earliest days in Paris, Vesalius had resented this custom. The sight of a barber hacking away at a muscle or blood vessel, often destroying the very structure he was supposed to be uncovering, infuriated the young man.

On one such occasion, the barber announced that the part he was looking for was not to be found. Sylvius then grumbled that mankind had apparently changed, and changed for the worse, since Galen's day. At this point the fiery-tempered Belgian could bear no more. He rose, walked over to the table, snatched the knife from the barber's hand, and skillfully uncovered the missing part. After a few such incidents the question of dissection was settled very sensibly. At the request of the professors and the students, the young foreigner took over the job completely. Sylvius, although he was undoubtedly jealous of Vesalius' skill, must have been pleased with this arrangement. It saved the price of a barber.

Vesalius had not been in Paris very long before he realized that he would never learn what he wanted to learn unless he took matters into his own hands. Copying notes from Galen and making an occasional dissection during a lecture could not satisfy his restless zeal for knowledge. He began to collect and dissect every animal he could get his hands on. But animals, he knew very well, were not the answer.

"The devil take the corpse of every pig that ever lived!" he said one day, looking up from the animal he was dissecting for the benefit of some fellow students. "I want to know what *men* are, not pigs! Believe me, my friends, there is only one book from which to learn about the human body, and that's the human body itself!"

There was a moment of shocked silence. Some of the students then made for the door as quickly as they could. The *human* body, he said. And just how did *he* intend to get his hands on a human body, when even the great professors of the University of Paris could hardly ever get hold of one? This Belgian was clearly headed for trouble. It would not be wise to be seen associating with him.

But some of his classmates stayed. The boldest of them said, "Could we really get hold of a human body?"

"I know where we could get some bones, anyway," Vesalius said eagerly. "There's a tavern half a square from the main gate of the Cemetery of the Innocents. Meet me there tonight at eleven."

From then on the young gentlemen of the University had a new sport to add to their already plentiful ways of getting into trouble with the townspeople. Vesalius and his friends made almost

nightly tours of Paris in search of material. They knew perfectly well what would happen to them if they were ever caught. But the greater the danger, the more they enjoyed it.

The grim hill of Montfaucon was a rich hunting ground. Here the bodies of all executed criminals were brought and hung from wooden beams. In the dark of the night such a place was not likely to attract crowds of passers-by. Except for a pack of wild dogs that once attacked them, the anatomy students had the place to themselves.

For bone-searching, the Cemetery of the Innocents was an unrivaled location. Here a rebuilding of the city walls had disturbed the bones of thousands of plague victims. Vesalius and his band turned up "an abundant supply," he later wrote. "Having learned by long and tiring observation, we, even blindfolded, dared at times to wager with our companions, and in the space of half an hour no bone could be offered us . . . which we could not identify by touch. This had to be done the more zealously by us who desired to learn inasmuch as there was a great lack of the assistance of teachers in this part of medicine."

In 1536 the French king, Francis I, on bad terms as usual with nearly every other king in Europe, came close to declaring war on the Emperor Charles V. Life in Paris became difficult for foreign students. Vesalius, who was a loyal subject of the Emperor Charles, left France. He returned to Belgium to study and then to lecture at the University of Louvain.

Now that he was teaching, Vesalius found the usual shortage of material more annoying than ever.

But he quickly introduced the students of Louvain to the Paris method of research. One night while he and his friend Regnier Gemma, a mathematician, were out prowling, he made the most spectacular find of his bone-hunting career.

Chained to a stake on the gallows hill he saw, to his astonishment, what was to all appearances a perfect and complete human skeleton. It was the remains of a criminal who had been burned at the stake. Birds of prey had been at work and had left nothing but the bare bones.

If Vesalius had just been handed a chest full of gold pieces he could not have been more excited. In a matter of seconds he was up on his friend's shoulders, eagerly reaching for the bones. "After I had brought the legs and arms home in secret and successive trips," he wrote, "I allowed myself to be shut out of the city in the evening in order to obtain the thorax which was firmly held by the chain. I was burning with so great a desire . . . that I was not afraid to snatch in the middle of the night what I so longed for. . . . The next day I transported the bones home piecemeal through another gate of the city."

A few days later a human skeleton, expertly wired together, was hung in the lecture hall. Vesalius answered suspicious questions by saying, "Oh, this? I had it sent from Paris."

He had not been in Louvain more than two years before he clashed with the most powerful and influential professor of the University. The subject of their dispute was the proper method of blood-letting, at that time the most controversial topic in all of medicine. Vesalius had already begun to grow restless in Louvain. Now that he had managed to make enemies of the entire medical faculty, he decided to seek his fortune elsewhere. He packed up his books, his notes, his drawings, and his bones, and headed south to Italy.

It was a wise move. The Italians, unlike the French, had no objections to the study of anatomy or the use of the human body for dissection, for the Church encouraged such study as a means of improving medical education. Less than a year after his arrival in Italy, Vesalius was appointed professor of surgery at the University of Padua. His duties included the teaching of anatomy. Vesalius was young for such an honor, the University faculty realized. But did that matter when you considered that he could sit blindfolded and identify any bone in the body simply by touching it? The wagers he had once made in the taverns of Paris were still paying handsomely.

Vesalius quickly became one of the most famous men in Italy. His lectures were an immediate success. Three weeks of intensive work, at twelve hours

a day, completed the course. A new series began
the day after the previous series ended. In addition
to the medical students, the hall was always
crowded with people who wanted to see the novel
sight of an anatomy professor dissecting and talking at the same time. And an anatomy professor
who rarely read from a book of Galen except to

point out some error in it! Vesalius' lectures became fashionable. The Italians of that period were hungering for new knowledge and new intellectual experiences, and these the Belgian professor certainly had to offer.

During his very first lectures at Padua, Vesalius introduced something absolutely new to his classes.

He drew and hung up in the hall large charts showing the veins, the arteries, and the nerves, so that the students could see at a glance what had once taken hours of explanation. The charts were such a success that the professor went a step further. He hired an artist named Jan Stefan van Kalkar, a pupil of the great Titian. Together the two men prepared six large plates of anatomical drawings. They were published in 1538. In an introduction to these unique charts, Vesalius wrote, "If I find this work is accepted . . . someday I hope to add something greater."

This was the first hint of a work that marks the turning point in the history of medicine and is, indeed, one of the landmarks in the development of human thought.

No one knows exactly when Vesalius decided to write his own book on anatomy—a book that would go for its authority not to tradition and hearsay, not to Galen or any other ancient writer, but to the human body itself. But the young professor began the actual work on it very shortly after his arrival in Italy.

His lecture fees alone were now bringing him much more money than he had ever had before. As his income grew, plans for his book became more and more elaborate. His labors were punctuated by violent arguments with the artist or artists who worked with him. Like many collaborators who need each other, the men got along very badly. Vesalius wrote angrily that the book had cost him a monstrous amount of work in directing the eye, the hand, and the intelligence of the artist. At times, he added, he had felt much more unfortunate than the criminal whose body he was dissecting.

This is only one side of the story. No doubt the artist—it was probably Jan Stefan van Kalkar—suffered too. Vesalius took revenge by refusing to mention his name at any point in the book. Future generations of scholars suffered from this whim. To this day no one is sure exactly who did the marvelous illustrations.

At last, in August of 1542, Vesalius sent the plates of the book across the Alps to Basel, Switzerland, with a long letter of instruction and pleading. He commended the project to the care of a certain John Oporinus, professor of Greek, who owned a fine printing press. The following January he himself arrived at Oporinus' shop to supervise the final steps. He watched, burning with impatience, as the last of the 701 magnificently printed pages came from the press. And at last he held the book in his hands:

Andreae Vesalii Bruxellensis
DE HUMANI CORPORIS FABRICA
Basileae, 1543

Andreas Vesalius of Brussels
ON THE STRUCTURE OF THE HUMAN BODY
Basel, 1543

"The greatest book ever written," said the revered Dr. William Osler, "from which modern medicine dates."

Vesalius' work is important not only because it was the first textbook of anatomy ever written. It stands supreme as the greatest work in the history of medicine because it showed, for the first time, what could be done when a man, relying on his eyes and his own brain, went straight to nature to learn the secrets of human life.

In 1628 a book was published that, together with Vesalius' *De Fabrica,* finally broke the power of ancient authority. The book was *An Anatomical Treatise on the Movement of the Heart and Blood in Animals, by William Harvey, the Englishman, Physician to the King.* It proved once and for all that the human body is the only true source of knowledge about itself.

Like the *De Fabrica,* Harvey's book caught the world unprepared. Harvey's theory was such a complete break with the traditional view—Galen's view—that people could not easily grasp it. To assert that blood moved in a circle was bad enough. But to claim that the *same* blood is used over and over again was not only an absurdity but an insult to nature herself. How long, after all, could a body remain healthy if the same old used-up blood was pumped through it again and again? " 'Twas believed by the vulgar that he was crack-brained," a historian of the times wrote, "and all the physicians were against him." Harvey's long life was nearly over before anyone began to take his work seriously.

Yet Harvey's proof of the circulation of the blood has been called "the greatest single discovery ever made about the human body." His little book did for physiology what Vesalius' did for anatomy. On these two foundation stones, modern medicine was built.

2

A M B R O I S E
P A R É

──────────── 1510 – 1590 ────────────

The Key to
Modern Surgery

In 1537, French troops, fighting in Italy, were camped outside the city of Turin. With the army was a young surgeon named Ambroise Paré. He was serving on his first military campaign. A few short months before he had been a barber's apprentice.

The practice of medicine in Paris, as Vesalius had found, was regulated by a stern and rigid code. At the top were the physicians of the powerful Faculty of Medicine. They were the University men, the undisputed masters of the profession.

Below them were the black-gowned surgeons. They were named "The Confraternity of St. Côme," in honor of their patron, but everyone called them "the surgeons of the long robe." Members of the

Confraternity did not actually perform operations. This was beneath their dignity. Their chief duties were those which the physicians found beneath *their* dignity: the application of surgical plasters, the treatment of wounds, and the use of the hot iron to stop bleeding.

Most of the actual work, little of the money, and none of the prestige went to the barber-surgeons. It was the barbers who, between haircutting and wig-curling, actually performed the bloodlettings and amputations that were ordered by the surgeons.

There was one step lower. At the absolute bottom of the scale came the barbers' apprentices. These were the boys with no money and no Latin, who could not attend the University. They learned their trade in the barber shop.

From their humble ranks came the father of modern surgery.

Ambroise Paré, our young barber-surgeon, had never been in a battle before. He had never treated gunshot wounds. For that matter, he had never seen one. But he knew what every authority on the subject had to say about them. Among the experts there was complete agreement. What did you do with a gunshot wound? You poured boiling oil over it. If the wound occurred in an arm or leg, you usually cut the arm or leg off, as quickly as possible. To stop the bleeding of the exposed blood vessels, you "sealed"

up the stump with a white-hot iron—the cautery.

These were the time-honored methods. These were the *only* methods. This was surgery as Ambroise Paré found it.

The idea of pouring boiling oil into the wounds of injured men seemed terrible to the young surgeon. But since he had not even taken the examination to qualify as a barber, he found it difficult to argue with every known expert on the subject. After the French army's first skirmish outside Turin, he summoned all his courage and dressed the wounded men with boiling oil. It was an experience as horrible as he had expected it to be.

When evening came he was still hard at work, and far from his base of supply. As he looked over the field, he saw dozens of wounded men still to be treated. He saw, too, that he had run out of oil.

These wounded men were poisoned. They would surely die unless their wounds were treated with boiling oil to combat the poison. But the only medication Paré had left was a soothing compound, called a "digestive," which he had invented to put on wounds already treated with boiling oil. It was made of turpentine, oil of roses, and egg yolk. For want of anything better, Paré dressed the rest of the wounds with this harmless preparation.

Paré slept very little that night. He was up before dawn the next morning to visit his patients, convinced that those who had been treated without oil would be dying or dead. Oddly enough, they were not. The other men, the ones who had been treated in the prescribed manner, were suffering the usual effects of gunshot wounds—pain, inflammation, sleeplessness. But their companions, the ones who should have been dying of poisoned wounds, were feeling remarkably well. They had even slept well most of the night, Paré was told. He peered under their bandages curiously. There was very little swelling and inflammation. For a moment he could do nothing but stare in disbelief at these men who were supposed to be dead and who were so obviously not.

The young surgeon was not at the moment sure just what he had proved or disproved. All he knew for a fact was that he would never again use boiling oil on gunshot wounds. A little later, when he had time to think things over, another idea came to him. The experts whom he had not dared to dispute had been just plain wrong about the boiling-oil treatment. Could they be wrong about other things too?

When the campaign was over, Paré returned to Paris. He soon married and tried to settle down. But the idea of being the proprietor of a barber shop did not appeal to him. In spite of his wife's natural objections, he determined to follow the fortunes of war. It was on the battlefields of the next thirty years that he did his great work for the world—his own world and ours.

In one way Ambroise Paré was not really suited to his chosen profession. He was much too kindhearted. He did not share the callous indifference with which many surgeons of his day viewed the misery of their patients. The discovery that laid the foundations of modern surgery was made because Ambroise Paré wished with all the fervor of his gentle heart to relieve the sufferings of wounded soldiers. The boiling-oil treatment he had discarded after his first day of battle. But there were other practices which he despised as much—the cautery, for example.

Cutting off a conscious man's leg was terrible in itself. To finish the job by plunging a white-hot poker into the wound was unspeakable. Of course there *was* another method of controlling bleeding— the bleeding, at least, of minor cuts and gashes. It was a very old method. Ancient writers, dating back to Galen, had made mention of it. But it was so simple that it seemed somehow ridiculous. Sixteenth-century surgeons thought it was a fable. They had never tried it because they were all con-

vinced that it would not work. They were convinced
that it would not work because none of them had ever
tried it to find out one way or the other.

But Ambroise Paré was no longer interested in
what other people thought was true. He wanted to
find out for himself. He began to make cautious
experiments with this simple and ridiculous method
of the ancients. He began talking about it too, and
then arguing about it.

How many times, he wondered one night, had
he argued about it? Around how many campfires?
And with how many opponents? Too many to remember them all, he decided. This was the year
1552 and the campfire was outside the town of
Danvilliers. His opponents were two young surgeons
out on their second campaign and quite convinced
that they had learned the whole art of surgery on
their first. And he had said it all so many times
before!

"We are cruel and inhuman, we surgeons," he
was telling them. "Why, we are no better than
that Roman fellow, Archagelus, who was stoned to
death by the people for the cruelty of his operations."

"We have heard you on this subject many times,
Master Ambroise," one of the young men said.

It was long past midnight. The moon had set

and the walls of the besieged town were barely visible through the darkness. There was no sound in the camp but the occasional whinny of a horse and the low voices of the three men.

"You will hear me on the subject again, I promise you," Paré said somberly.

"And what subject is it that keeps you awake at such an unfriendly hour, gentlemen?" The three surgeons struggled to their feet. The voice was that of Monsieur de Rohan, the company commander, who had the habit of roaming around the camp at odd hours. He sat down by the fire.

"The subject, Monsieur, is a fanciful invention of Master Ambroise. It is part of a quaint theory he holds about surgery. We have to discuss *theories* of surgery at night. By day we are too busy with the *practice* of it!" The young man laughed, pleased at his own joke. Paré smiled, for his quaint theories were well known to his old friend Rohan. "Master Ambroise," the young man continued, "would have us abandon the use of the cautery in favor of this invention."

"Oh?" said Rohan. "And what *is* this fanciful invention with which Master Ambroise plans to replace the cautery?"

The young man sat up straight. "A thread and a needle! Fancy—a thread such as a housewife uses to sew a rent in her skirt. A piece of string doing the work of the cautery! You can see that it is impossible, Monsieur."

Paré opened his mouth to protest. But before he could speak Rohan said, "That may be. I know little of surgery or, for that matter, of sewing up skirts. But tell me—if a man bleeds, it is because of an open wound of one sort or another, is it not?"

Paré sat back smiling. The matter was in good hands.

The young man said, "That would seem to be the idea, Monsieur."

"The cautery, then, is actually used to close the edge of a wound?"

"Exactly, Monsieur," the young man replied.

"In other words," Rohan went on, "one must close a wound by searing the edges together?"

"Exactly, Monsieur."

There was a short pause. Monsieur Rohan had a good sense of timing. "But it seems to me—as a layman, mind you—that one might just as well close a wound by sewing the edges together."

The young man was taken aback by this turn of the conversation. He could only stammer, "But it is impossible, Monsieur. As a surgeon, I assure you that this invention of Master Ambroise's is—"

"This invention of Master Ambroise's, now that

I recall, I have seen with my own eyes," Rohan said smoothly. "It was used on a man with a gash the length of his forehead. He was bleeding like a fountain. Then his head was sewn up—the way a housewife sews up her skirt, did you say?—and the bleeding stopped."

Paré said, "I remember the incident, Monsieur. The man did stop bleeding, yes. But to call this method 'Master Ambroise's invention' is to do me too much honor. I invented neither the needle nor the thread, nor the use of them. Actually, the ligature, as it is called, was in use in the days of Galen. I have used it since with great success. Can you understand what that means, gentlemen? A needle and thread instead of the hot iron!"

"Oh, come, Master Ambroise, you are too lyrical," the younger man said. "So you have occasionally healed a cut or removed a splinter without cauterizing. And for this you talk of abandoning the cautery altogether. It is surgery we are speaking of, Monsieur, surgery." He added significantly, "Just how would you cut off a man's leg and avoid using the cautery, Master Ambroise?"

There was a long silence. "How would I, indeed?" Paré said slowly. He had no answer, although the young man had stumbled onto the question that was seldom out of Paré's mind. For if you talked about surgery in 1552, you were talking about amputations, the chief employment of the military surgeon. If a new method of controlling bleeding could not be used after an amputation, it was simply not worth discussing. And no surgeon, ancient or modern, Paré knew, had ever done an amputation without using a hot iron to close the wound.

Rohan now got to his feet and said, "It is nearly dawn. They are sleeping late beyond the walls. I have grown rather fond of their little five o'clock salvo. One can tell the time of day by it so conveniently." He walked slowly toward his tent.

Paré stretched. "Well, gentlemen," he began, "we must talk some other—" There was a blaze of musket fire from the wall. "Ah," said the surgeon. "Monsieur de Rohan now knows what time it is." He yawned.

A messenger wearing the Rohan livery ran up to the three men. "Master Ambroise! You must come at once!"

"Monsieur de Rohan?" Paré asked sharply, leaping to his feet.

"No, but in his tent—" The boy scurried back into the darkness.

Paré exchanged a quick look with his two colleagues and nodded toward the tent where his instruments were kept. Then he followed the messenger.

He found Rohan pacing up and down impatiently. "The enemy spies are doing their work too well—unless their gunners sent a bullet through the walls of my tent by sheer coincidence. A good piece of marksmanship spoiled only by the fact that I was not in the tent. But—" He nodded at the young man who lay on the ground at the door of the tent. Paré recognized him as a member of Rohan's staff. His left leg had been shattered by the bullet. He appeared to be unconscious. But, hearing Paré's voice whispering something to Rohan, he opened his eyes and tried to speak.

Paré knelt down beside him and said, "This was an unlucky night, Monsieur. But in a very short moment the worst of it will be over."

There was comprehension in the man's face, and then fear—the same fear that Paré had seen in so many faces. No soldier going into battle, however great the danger, ever had that look on his face. It was reserved for him and his hot iron.

The two young surgeons came hurrying into the tent with Paré's instruments. Paré said, "The light in here is impossible. We must get him outside!"

They carried the soldier, now fully conscious, outside and laid him near a dying campfire. One of the young surgeons rekindled it. Then he selected a cautery from one of Paré's boxes and began to heat it.

An amputation had to be done quickly. It was

with good reason that a surgeon's skill was judged by his speed. Paré had made his incision and sawed through the bone almost before the cautery in the fire began to glow. Only three minutes had passed since the beginning of the operation.

Now Paré looked from the contorted face of the patient to the glowing cautery. "No!" he said, waving away the hot iron that the other man was holding out to him. He turned to his supply box

and pulled out two pieces of strong thread.

Exactly what happened then the two other surgeons could not later remember. They saw Paré's head bent over the patient and his hands working at twice their usual speed. Then they saw that the stump which should have been spurting blood was not spurting blood, although there was nothing to prevent the bleeding but two pieces of thread tied around two blood vessels.

The whole action had passed so quickly that the young surgeon found himself still trying to hand the hot iron to Paré.

Paré looked at it for a moment and then said, "No, my friend, I have no need of it—now or ever again." He began gathering his instruments together. His hands were shaking, now that the operation was over and he could allow them to shake.

"I returned to Paris with my gentleman whose leg I had cut off," Paré wrote later. "I dressed him and God healed him. I sent him to his house, merry, with a wooden leg, and he was content, saying that he had got off cheap not to have been miserably burned to stop the blood."

The discovery that bleeding in major surgery could be controlled by the use of the ligature was the greatest discovery that had yet been made in surgery. Paré had laid the foundation on which all its future progress was built.

3

EDWARD
JENNER

——————— 1749 – 1823 ———————

The Conquest
of Smallpox

The milkmaid who sat smiling at Dr. Ludlow's
new apprentice was young and very pretty. Or so
the new apprentice thought as he sat in a corner
of his master's consulting room, watching the proceedings with interest. Dr. Ludlow, while bandag-
ing the girl's finger, was lecturing to her on the
failing health of the British population. It did not
bother him in the least that the milkmaid was flirt-
ing with his apprentice and paying no attention at
all to his speech.

"Don't know what we're coming to," he rumbled
on. "Here we are in the modern age! The year
1766! Progress everywhere you look. And we're an
unhealthier lot than our great-grandparents were.
Twenty more buried last week." He paused long

enough to tie the last knot in the bandage. "Pox got 'em! Never know who'll be next! Could be anybody." Cheerfully he added, "Could be you! *Then* that pretty skin of yours wouldn't look so pretty!"

At that the girl turned to him quickly. "Smallpox?" she said. "Bless you, no, sir! I cannot take that disease."

"And why not, pray, Missy?"

"I've had the cowpox!" she said proudly, as though it were a personal triumph.

Dr. Ludlow grunted. This popular superstition of the village milkmaids had always amused him. They actually believed, poor ignorant girls, that a case of cowpox—the mild animal disease which all dairy people caught at one time or another—would protect them against smallpox. "Edward," he said to the boy, "you hear that? Don't forget it! Whenever you go visiting your patients, take a cow with you! Wonderful animal, the cow!" The good man appreciated his humor more than either member of his audience. He roared with delight. The girl pouted. Young Edward Jenner smiled.

But that moment led eventually to the control of smallpox, the deadliest disease then known to mankind. For Edward Jenner was a man who took knowledge where he found it. For years he would store it away in his memory that the village milkmaids had clear complexions, unmarked by the vicious disease, and that they believed themselves to be safe from smallpox.

When Edward Jenner had learned all that old Dr. Ludlow could teach him, he went to London to study with John Hunter, the foremost surgeon of his day and one of the greatest scientific investigators of all time. Hunter quickly recognized the boy's talent. When Jenner had finished his formal studies, the famous doctor offered to hire him as an assistant. At the same time the renowned explorer of the South Seas, Captain James Cook, invited him to come along on a forthcoming expedition as ship's naturalist.

It was a flattering choice for a country boy to have to make. But because he *was* a country boy at heart as well as in fact, Edward Jenner declined both offers and went home to the quiet village that he loved. Here he married, settled down, and devoted himself to the broken bones, measles, and babies of his country neighbors. And thus his life might have run to the end—except for an idea.

"I cannot take that disease. I've had the cowpox!" a milkmaid had said, years before. Jenner knew that smallpox itself would protect against smallpox, for having once had the disease you were safe from it forever after. Inoculation had been a custom in England for some years. This was the practice of injecting matter from a smallpox pustule into a healthy person. Artificially induced smallpox was milder, people thought, than genuinely "caught" smallpox. The theory was good. The practice left much to be desired. Inoculation was a terrible ordeal in itself. It had, moreover, the effect of keeping Europe in a state of epidemic for years. There was enough smallpox around without purposely making new cases.

But would the harmless cowpox also give immunity to smallpox?

In London, Jenner had put the question to John Hunter. "Do you think that cowpox really prevents smallpox?"

Most London doctors would have laughed at the question. But John Hunter had a theory about the teaching of medicine. He never said, "No!" when a pupil asked him whether something could be done. He said instead, "Science is unlimited. Perhaps." And to Jenner, who had asked a question to which he did not know the answer, Hunter said, "Don't think! *Try!* Be patient. Be accurate."

Since the time had not come to try, Jenner continued to think. He talked, too. His friends began to get a little bored with his endless conversation about cowpox. The medical men among them grew angry as well as bored. "A man in your position," they told Edward Jenner, "should not be building scientific theory on the gossip of dairymaids!"

And so, when Jenner was ready to turn the tantalizing idea into a fully formed medical opinion, he stated it first not to a fellow physician but to a poet. A poet, he felt, would understand wild, unlikely ideas much more easily than a scientist. It was in May of 1782. Jenner was riding on the road from Gloucester to Bristol with his friend Edward Gardner. He began to talk about cowpox, hesitantly at first. Gardner smiled to himself in the darkness, amused that his friend should be thinking about cows on this starlit spring night. But he grunted encouragingly. What he had never dared to say outright to any of his medical colleagues, Jenner said to the poet.

"Gardner, I believe that there is one type of cowpox that will give protection against smallpox. I hope—and it has become more than a hope—that some day the practice of producing this cowpox in human beings will spread all over the world. When that day comes there will be no more smallpox."

Jenner now set out to prove this theory. His friends were willing and eager to point out the flaws in it. There was a milkmaid in Kingscote with smallpox, a colleague assured him. She had had the cowpox the year before. A farmer's boy in Gloucester had recently died of smallpox—after a serious case of cowpox the month before.

How could he explain these cases and the others that came to his attention? Certain patients had definitely been infected with cowpox. Later they had died of smallpox. Didn't this prove that Jenner's theory was wrong?

It took him nearly five years to answer this question. He made a complete study of all dairy diseases and found that cows are victims of quite an assortment of ills. Many of these cow diseases produced running sores on the hands of the milkers. All of these sores were called "cowpox." But Jenner believed that only one kind was the preventive against smallpox. He divided the dairy diseases into two categories: "true" cowpox and "spurious," or false, cowpox.

So *that* was all there was to it, said a colleague with whom Jenner was talking one day. Then how did he explain the dairy in Newport that had had an epidemic of the "true" cowpox last month and was now undergoing a siege of smallpox?

Jenner went at once to Newport. Had it really been cowpox, true cowpox? "Oh, yes, Dr. Jenner," the dairyman assured him. "All the real symptoms you told us about." And was it true that some of the milkers now had smallpox? The man nodded at the freshly turned earth in the churchyard across the road.

This seemed to be perfect clinical proof that Jenner was wrong. But he did not give up.

He began all over again, with a careful examination of all the local cows. Here was a case of true cowpox, and a bad one. This was the height of the disease, Jenner decided, rubbing the animal's ears sympathetically. Here was another case. It was nearly over, from the look of the sores. Cowpox has stages, he thought, just as smallpox does. Suppose the infectious matter in the sore was different during the different stages of the disease. Suppose that after a certain period, the matter could still cause eruptions on the hands of the workers but could not protect them against smallpox.

Between the long, night-and-day hours which he devoted to his patients, he began a new study of hundreds of cows and milkers in various stages of cowpox. Another five years passed, then six, and eight, and nine. The result of his research? A knowledge that true cowpox has certain well-marked stages of development.

On May 14, 1796, a milkmaid named Sarah Nelmes walked into Jenner's office. She had a bad case of cowpox, she told the doctor. Her employer had sent her around to have her hand bandaged. Jenner saw that she had an ugly, running sore, a cowpox pustule at the very peak of its development. He had seen hundreds of cases of cowpox at

dairies, but he had never before been asked to treat one in his office.

As Jenner looked at the girl's hand the voice of the now dead John Hunter was in his ear, as clearly as if the man had been standing by his side. "Don't think! *Try!*" He had been thinking for fourteen years. Surely it was time to try!

His meditations were interrupted by the sound of shouts and laughter. He looked out the window. The caretaker's children were playing tag in the garden outside his office. James, the eldest, was a

healthy-looking boy of eight. Jenner watched the child for a moment, then went to the door and called, "James! Will you step in here for a few minutes, please?"

One of the most significant events in history was then accomplished—by the milkmaid, the boy, and the country doctor. Jenner took some of the matter from the sore on the girl's hand and scratched it into the arm of the boy. It was the first vaccination.

James developed a mild case of cowpox, as scheduled. The experiment was half over. On July 1, Jenner inoculated him with infectious matter taken from a smallpox victim. Since smallpox inoculation was a widespread custom of the time, this was not an unusual action.

Two weeks later he wrote to his friend the poet:

Dear Gardner,

As I promised to let you know how I proceeded in my inquiry into the nature of that singular disease, the cowpox . . . you will be gratified to hear that I have at length accomplished what I have been so long waiting for—the passing of the vaccine virus from one human being to another by the ordinary mode of inoculation.

A boy by the name of Phipps was inoculated in the arm from a pustule on the hand of a young woman who was infected by her master's cows. . . .

But now listen to the most delightful part of my story. The boy has since been inoculated for the smallpox, which, as I ventured to predict, produced no effects. I shall now pursue my experiments with redoubled ardour.

Jenner, still cautious, repeated the experiment twenty-three times more before he published his results in a historic paper which he called *An Inquiry into the Causes and Effects of the Variolae Vaccinae*. Vaccinia, the scientific name for cowpox, comes from the Latin word for cow.

A great furor followed the announcement. It was fed by wild rumors about children who had been vaccinated and had promptly begun to moo. But soon, because the need was so desperate, the attitude began to change. The self-effacing country doctor found himself the most talked-about man in the world. It took three secretaries to handle the mail that poured in. Every day brought requests for vaccine lymph, reports on cases, questions about the proper method, letters of congratulation, and crackpot letters urging him to repent his folly. "I have become vaccine clerk to the world," he said to Gardner one afternoon, as he leafed through the mailbag.

Very soon there was no part of the world that had not taken up vaccination. France, Germany, Spain, and Austria were the first. The news was

carried to Greece and spread from there to Tur-
key, Armenia, and the Far East. In 1803 the Spanish government sent a naval expedition to carry
vaccine lymph to the far-flung Spanish possessions
in South America and the Caribbean. The expedition then moved on to China. India, the last
stronghold of smallpox, urgently requested lymph,
which was finally sent from Vienna.

News of Jenner's discovery had reached the
United States with the publication of his *Inquiry*.
The new nation was cool to the idea at first. But
when President Thomas Jefferson had himself vaccinated, the popularity of the discovery was assured.

Honors and gifts from all over the world came to
Jenner. The Empress of Russia sent him a dia-
mond ring. An American Indian chief sent him a
wampum belt. The French Emperor, Napoleon, although he was at war with England, released two
British prisoners when he learned that they were
friends of Edward Jenner. In Germany, May 14—
the date of James Phipps's vaccination—was de-
clared a yearly national holiday.

But in England, Jenner was plagued by the petty
jealousy of his colleagues, the powerful physicians
of London. They could never quite stomach the
fuss that was being made over the country doctor.
When he was nominated for membership in the
the Royal College of Physicians, it was voted that

he could not be admitted until he had taken the
usual examination in Latin. "And that," he said,
"I will not do for the whole of John Hunter's mu-
seum!"

The sharp voices of his critics meant little to Jenner when he read the statistics that were sent in after a trial period of two years. In Havana, for example, there had not been a single death from smallpox in the two-year period. And Havana had once had the highest smallpox death rate in the world. In Milan, no deaths; in Vienna, no deaths; in Denmark, Norway, and Sweden, no deaths. In the whole of South America, no deaths.

"I hope that some day the practice of producing cowpox in human beings will spread over the whole world," he had once said to Gardner. "When that day comes, there will be no more smallpox."

There was more than "no smallpox." The country doctor who was not too proud to find wisdom in the tradition of his people had brought an entirely new concept to medical practice—the doctrine of preventive medicine.

4

RENÉ THÉOPHILE LAËNNEC

1781 – 1826

The Science of Diagnosis

"Pneumonia."

"I believe that you are wrong, Monsieur. This is a case of empyema."

"Pneumonia!"

"Empyema!"

The man whose chest condition was under discussion looked from one side of his bed to the other. What a peculiar pair of doctors, he thought. He wished they would make up their minds and go away.

"Pneumonia!" thundered François Joseph Victor Broussais. He was a huge hulk of a man, well known in Parisian medical and social circles. He was both prosperous and well connected.

"Empyema!" shouted René Théophile Laënnec.

He was five feet three inches tall, and so thin that
—as he himself put it—he seemed barely capable of
casting a shadow. He was a poor provincial doctor, just twenty years old, who had walked over
two hundred miles from his home in Nantes for a
chance to study with the famous professors of medicine in Paris. The most famous of them all was
Jean Nicolas Corvisart.

Now that he was here, Laënnec was not sure it
had been such a good idea. He had no money
and no connections. And it seemed to the gentle,
good-natured young man from the provinces that
he would never understand his sophisticated Paris
colleagues and their alarmingly quick tempers. He
had never expected to be dragged into a quarrel
with one of them over a matter as impersonal as
a difference in diagnosis. But here he was!

At this moment, Corvisart walked in. The students, waiting to make ward rounds with him,
snapped to attention. Although the great professor
was not in himself a forbidding sight, his exalted
position as physician to Napoleon had a subduing
effect on people.

"Is something wrong, gentlemen?" he asked the
students.

After a few moments of silence, Broussais said,
"Nothing serious. A slight difference of opinion with

one of your new students." He chuckled over the last words. "About this patient's pneumonia."

"Empyema," Laënnec said softly.

Corvisart looked at the young man and smiled. Of all the students in the ward, he would have picked Laënnec as the one least likely to stand up to Broussais. "Well, gentlemen, no need to fight about it. There is a better way to settle the argument." He turned to the students. "Empyema, as you know, is a collection of pus in the pleural cavity. It is distinct from pneumonia but often confused with it in over-hasty diagnosis. Bring me a trocar, please."

An assistant handed him a hollow needle. Within a few seconds Corvisart had inserted it beween the ribs of the patient. He drew it out, examined the needle, and then turned to Laënnec. "You are right, Monsieur—what is your name? There is considerable pus present in the pleural cavity. This is empyema."

Laënnec nodded and said nothing. Broussais turned on his heel and stalked out of the room. The incident was quickly forgotten by everyone except the two men. But René Théophile Laënnec had made his first impression on Paris. After such a long walk, there was some satisfaction in that.

In 1802, just a year later, Laënnec wrote a paper on the diagnosis of peritonitis, a disease that had been puzzling doctors for years. In this paper the 21-year-old student said not only everything in the way of clinical description that could be said on the subject at that time, but nearly everything that can be said on it today. With his first piece of research he had won a place among the notable names of medicine. But he had barely begun. Paper after paper appeared in the medical journals, each one a masterpiece of precise observation. Even the sophisticated medical circles of Paris began to take notice. In those days doctors knew very little about distinguishing one disease from another. The science of diagnosis had not yet begun to exist, and Laënnec's work was a revelation.

As the years passed, Laënnec found his interest settling around diseases of the heart and lungs. From Corvisart he learned a valuable new trick originated by an Austrian physician named Leopold Auenbrugger. As a boy, Auenbrugger had often watched his father, an innkeeper, tap beer kegs to learn from the pitch of the note the level of the liquid inside. When he had grown up and become the physician to the Empress Maria Theresa, Auenbrugger remembered the beer kegs in the inn at Graz. He hit upon the simple idea that if you tap a human chest—which is not unlike a barrel in shape—you might tell from the sound of

the note whether there was any liquid inside and where. At autopsies he had seen lungs filled with fluid, lungs half solidified, lungs with holes in them. To find out these things at an autopsy, the doctor thought, did not help the patient very much.

Auenbrugger began tapping the chest of every patient he saw. He was a musician, and his sensitive ear now became doubly useful. Here was a man dying of tuberculosis. Certain spots on his chest gave out a high-pitched sound when Auenbrugger tapped them. The man died shortly thereafter, and Auenbrugger found fluid in his chest at the site of each high note. Here was another patient whose chest produced the same odd, cracked sound produced by striking a cracked plate. At the autopsy the physician found cavities in the lungs. He named the sound "cracked-pot resonance," a description that stands today.

Laënnec saw great possibilities in Auenbrugger's method. It made the diagnosis of chest diseases more precise than it had ever been. He wished that some similar method could be found for studying the sounds of breathing and the sounds made by patients' hearts.

For in those days there was no way to listen to a patient's heart except to place one's ear directly against the chest wall. One could then hear faint thumping sounds, indicating that the heart was beating. In the presence of a live patient, this information was not particularly useful.

But one day the little doctor found to his chagrin that even the simple process of placing one's ear against a patient's chest had complications. It was 1816. Laënnec had become chief of staff at the Necker Hospital. One afternoon he was called in to examine a newly admitted patient, a young lady with all the symptoms of angina pectoris, a disease of the heart. Laënnec was afraid of all women and of the young ones in particular. He found, when face to face with this patient, that he could not work up the moral courage necessary to put his ear against her heart. "Even if I did," he told himself, "I couldn't hear much because she's so fat. Why do women let themselves get so fat?"

Now here was a dilemma—a patient with possible heart trouble, and no way, not even the most elementary, of listening to her heart. Laënnec decided that he needed some fresh air, so he took a walk through the nearby gardens of the Louvre to think things over. The lovely park was crowded with children. He stopped to watch a group of them playing.

Four boys were gathered around a seesaw of light wood. One of them had found a pin and was scratching one end of the board. His companions, their ears pressed to the other end of the board, squealed with delight at the clearness and loudness with which the sound of the scratching traveled through the wood. "What makes it do that? What makes it do that?" the smallest boy cried, jumping up and down with excitement.

Laënnec laughed. He walked over to them, feeling a friendly impulse to explain the phenomenon. It was such a simple principle of acoustics. "Well, you see," he began "when sound passes through a solid object, it is magnified, and so—"

Then he stopped. What had he said? "When sound passes through a solid object, it is magnified—" Of course! He turned and ran back to the hospital as fast as his short legs could carry him.

He stopped, seized a stack of ordinary writing paper, and then burst in unannounced on his overweight patient. To the amazement of the young lady and of the nurse who had followed him into the ward, he rolled up the paper tightly. Then he placed one end of the cylinder over the patient's heart and the other end to his ear.

Not until later, when his excitement had subsided, did he realize that he was the first man who had ever heard the sound of the human lungs as well as the human heart.

Laënnec left the patient and hurried into the next ward, still clutching the roll of paper. Here was a man with pneumonia. Through the paper

cylinder, Laënnec could hear loud, thick sounds of
breathing. In the next bed was a man with empyema. Laënnec listened and heard no sound at all.
Well, he thought, remembering an earlier incident,
no one ever had to be confused over these two diseases again! The patient said petulantly, "What

are you doing, Doctor?" Through the cylinder his voice had an odd, tremulous quality, like the bleating of a goat. Aegophony, Laënnec called it later.

In the next ward was a woman with tuberculosis. Listening to her chest, Laënnec heard a curious thing. When she spoke, the sound of her voice seemed to issue directly from the chest wall. He realized that a cavity in the lungs must be responsible. He called the phenomenon "pectoriloquy"— speaking through the chest.

The wards were full of the sound of disease, each sound as distinct to his sensitive ear as the notes of his own flute.

A roll of paper was not a proper scientific device. So Laënnec borrowed a lathe and made himself a simple wooden cylinder with a narrow canal running down the center of it. Now he had a real, new instrument. It needed a name. His elderly uncle, to whom he submitted the problem, thought it might be called the "thoracoscope," from the Latin *thorax,* chest, and the Greek *skopein,* to examine. But Laënnec was a classical scholar as well as a doctor. He would not mix Latin and Greek so carelessly. The idea was good, though. He substituted the Greek equivalent of *thorax,* which is *stethos.* He called his roll of wood a "stethoscope."

But he never used the name himself. To him the wooden cylinder was always the "baton." Marshals of the French army carried their batons as insignia of their rank. This roll of wood was the baton of his own personal war.

No man has ever used his own discovery better than Laënnec. Within three years he had classified and described every sound made by the human lung in disease. Then, since no one outside the Necker Hospital knew anything about the stethoscope, he began to write a full account of the discovery. He found the work extremely tiring, for he was already beginning to suffer the terrible fatigue so familiar to him from the histories of his tuberculous patients. But in August of 1819 his book appeared. It consisted of two volumes, called *On Mediate Auscultation*. With the stethoscope that went with it, it cost sixteen francs. The book stands with the works of Vesalius and Harvey as one of the great foundation stones of modern medicine.

Laënnec's ideas spread through the influence of important patients. Madame de Chateaubriand had a cough and fever. Her physicians diagnosed tuberculosis and gave her three months to live. Laënnec, with his baton, appeared on the scene and said that Madame had a bad cold. To the chagrin of his rivals, Madame recovered. Soon Laënnec was listening to the chest rattles of the royal family itself.

But although his patients, both rich and poor,

were wholly devoted to the gentle little man, he had bitter enemies among those who opposed his discovery. At the head of the opposition party was a man with a long memory.

Age had not improved François Joseph Victor Broussais. He was richer and more successful now, but he was essentially the same bully he had been eighteen years before. For all these years Broussais had remembered a day on which a ridiculous little man named Laënnec had made a fool of him. And one day in August of 1819 he read a book by this same Laënnec, called *On Mediate Auscultation.* And what had this Laënnec done but recount the incident in print! The names were disguised, of course, but Broussais recognized himself only too well. He knew that other people would recognize him too.

The two men became involved in one of the bitterest medical feuds of all time.

Broussais believed firmly in a doctrine of his own invention. He called it "physiological medicine." According to this theory, all disease was caused by irritation somewhere in the body. There was no such thing as different diseases; there was only a different amount of irritation. The king of all ailments was inflammation of the intestinal tract. All other so-called diseases were nothing but sympathy pains. Much more was at stake, therefore, than hurt pride. Laënnec claimed a difference between diseases so marked that one could actually tell one from another simply by listening through a tube! This idea, if swallowed, would be a terrible blow to "physiological medicine." And "physiological medicine" was paying off splendidly. Broussais swore that he would crush Laënnec.

Soon open controversy was raging, Broussais lecturing against Laënnec and Laënnec lecturing against Broussais. The big man had the advantage. He was a clever orator. When he made references, as he frequently did, to "the little Laënnec" or "the tiny professor," his listeners roared with laughter. The more they laughed, the less they thought. The less they thought, the more sensible Broussais' theories seemed to them. Although Laënnec fought back as hard as he could, he was too weak to lecture very often, and he was not an impressive speaker.

Laënnec often heard himself jeered in public. Children thought it good fun to run after him in the street, laughing at his physique, as they had heard their parents doing. And as Broussais had intended, people began to laugh at Laënnec's theories too. Tuberculosis contagious? Ridiculous! Tuberculosis caused by a specific agent? What kind of specific agent? Soon Monsieur Laënnec would be telling them that there were little creatures

floating around in the air that gave people tuberculosis!

The division in the medical world caused by the fight between Broussais and Laënnec was so great that it lasted for nearly sixty years. But it took only five years of it to complete the breakdown of

Laënnec's failing health. As he came to understand that there was very little time left to him, he was seized by a terrible longing for his home, and in May of 1826 he took his last leave of Paris.

He reached Brittany so exhausted that he was not expected to live out the week. The local doctors were called in. They listened gravely through their colleague's stethoscope and said that they heard nothing abnormal. He smiled at that and said, "But if I could listen, I know that I would hear it."

Because Laënnec was sick and shrunken in his last years, people forgot how young he was when he died. He had lived only forty-five years, but he had had time enough to turn the course of medicine into new channels. For Laënnec gave far more to medicine than the wooden cylinder which would become the present chromium-and-rubber trademark of the profession. He gave system and method to what had once been the most haphazard part of the doctor's work. We have come a long way since his time, with our elaborate devices—the X-ray, the electrocardiogram, the laboratory with its vast facilities for uncovering hidden disease. But the science of diagnosis really dates from this good little man with his penetrating mind, his sensitive ear— and his incurable timidity.

5

WILLIAM
MORTON

—————— 1819 – 1868 ——————

The Discovery
of Anesthesia

In Boston, Massachusetts, there lived an ambitious dentist named William Morton who was looking for a new way to fit false teeth. Recently married and usually short of cash, the young man had visions of making his fortune by improving the dentures of New England. But there was one serious drawback. His method involved removing the original teeth, root and all. And in 1844 having all your teeth pulled out was a painful experience. Morton had watched more than one patient stalk out of the office and vow that he would never again show his face at Number 19 Tremont Row.

Some way, Morton decided, would have to be found to pull a tooth painlessly. If he could find the way, he would be the richest dentist in Boston.

From this commercial motive came surgical anesthesia, a gift for which mankind had searched for centuries in vain.

The young dentist experimented with brandy, champagne, opium, and hypnotism, which was then called mesmerism. None of them worked, and very shortly he reached a sensible conclusion. If the greatest scientific minds in the world had failed to solve the problem, it was unlikely that he, William Morton, could work it out after studying dentistry for only eighteen months.

On Somerset Street, not far away, lived a learned physician, chemist, geologist, and traveler named Charles Thomas Jackson. Such a man, Morton thought, could teach him a great deal. He enrolled as a student in the doctor's office, as was the custom then. He devoted his spare evenings to reading Jackson's books and talking to the eminent doctor.

On one of these evenings the talk turned, as it often did, to Morton's professional problems. "Killing the dental nerve," Morton was saying to his teacher, "is sometimes the only way to save a tooth. But it's too painful to be very practical."

Jackson laughed. "You should try some of my toothache drops."

"Toothache drops? What are they?"

"Just ether. Ethyl oxide, liquid, strong- smelling, discovered by Paracelsus, used as an asthma remedy," he added, remembering that he was supposed to be teaching the young man medicine. "I rubbed it on a sore tooth for a man once. Trouble was, it helped him so much that he kept sending his friends around to me. I didn't want to get stuck with *that* kind of practice—no offense, Morton! I haven't used the stuff in years."

"Ether—" Morton said thoughtfully. It was worth a try.

On the next day a nervous lady named Miss Parrott appeared at Number 19 Tremont Row. She had traveled from Gloucester, she said timidly, to let Dr. Morton look at her cavity. But she was afraid of dentists. Was there *no* way, she inquired, to fill a tooth painlessly?

Morton considered the question briefly. "There's something I can try," he said, taking a newly purchased bottle of ether from the shelf.

He poured some of the strong-smelling liquid over Miss Parrott's tooth and went to work. Miss Parrott wrinkled her nose, but although he scraped away vigorously at the tooth not a groan escaped the sensitive lady. He took a probe and pressed it gently into the gum surrounding the ailing tooth. There was still no reaction from Miss Parrott.

When the tooth was filled he made a pretense of puttering around the office for a few minutes. Then he jabbed the gum again.

Miss Parrott shrieked.

When she had left the office, Morton sat down and stared at the bottle of ether. For some reason the vile-smelling stuff had made her gum temporarily numb. The effect was temporary, of course, because the ether turned from a liquid to a gas so quickly and floated away. But could the whole body be brought under the influence of ether—by inhaling it, for example?

"Can ether be inhaled?" Morton asked Jackson.

"Of course. I told you it was used as an asthma remedy. It won't hurt you if you take just a little of it."

Suppose you took more than just a little, Morton wondered. What would happen to you then?

In the woods around his father-in-law's farm he caught half a dozen squirrels and rabbits, and one by one made them inhale the vapor of ether. The experiment produced perfect results: they all died. Ether killed them. That, Morton decided, certainly answered his question. Ether would undoubtedly kill his patients too. Naturally a patient could not complain of pain if he were dead.

There the matter might have ended if Morton had not finally scraped together the necessary money to enter the Harvard Medical School—this while carrying on a large dental practice and raising a family! As a medical student, he attended lectures and demonstrations at the Massachusetts General Hospital. And in December of 1845 the dentist who was fretting about painless tooth-pulling watched a man have his leg cut off. The surgeon was John Collins Warren.

Dr. Warren was a great surgeon, a description which in those days meant—just as it had meant in the days of Ambroise Paré—that he was a fast surgeon. For the best that a surgeon could do for his patient, besides giving him a stick of wood to bite, was to work fast.

To Morton, watching and listening in horror, the day was one of great significance. He had seen with his own eyes how terrible and how bitter was the need for just the thing he had been looking for. And he had thought of it in terms of fitting teeth! He would take up his experiments where he had left them. And this time, he vowed with Yankee determination, he would succeed.

Two years earlier his former dental partner, Horace Wells, had done some promising experiments with nitrous oxide gas, but nothing had come of them. Morton, after considering further investigation of the gas, decided to give ether another chance. He had given up too easily, he decided. In his textbooks of pharmacy he read that there were different kinds of ether—chloric and sulphuric. Had he used the wrong kind on the squirrels and rabbits? He had also read that the drug would cause stupefaction if taken too freely. But between stupefaction and death, might there not be another, undiscovered state of being?

He bought a four-ounce bottle of pure sulphuric ether and took it home. Assuring himself that his wife was out of earshot, he lured the family dog, a trusting spaniel, to a deserted spot in the garden and presented him with an ether-soaked sponge.

Within a few seconds the dog was completely limp. Morton stared at the inert body in amazement. The spaniel was really unconscious, wasn't he? Not just stupefied, but really asleep? Or maybe . . . He prodded the dog nervously. If the animal failed to revive, Elizabeth would never forgive him. Morton shook the dog vigorously.

The spaniel opened his eyes, staggered to his feet, and cast one reproachful look at his master. Then he tottered into the fish pond to wake himself up. Here for the first time was a really satisfactory result.

The next day the dentist arranged to have his friend and colleague, Grenville Hayden, take over his practice so that Morton could devote himself entirely to his research. He began his experiments by inhaling a mixture of ether and opium, with no results. He tried giving ether to the dog again. But once had been enough for the spaniel, who refused to cooperate. Morton offered his two young apprentices five dollars if they could find someone willing to be experimented on for a fee. The boys covered the Faneuil Hall district and the waterfront without success. No one was interested in their suspicious offer.

Perhaps the boys would take ether themselves, Morton suggested, fingering a five-dollar bill. Young Leavitt agreed, daring his friend to join him. The two boys inhaled some ether. After a little giggling and capering about the room, the boys sobered up without showing the least interest in sleeping. Something was wrong. But what? Morton sniffed the ether in the jug suspiciously. "You're sure this is pure sulphuric ether?" he asked Leavitt.

"Yes, Doctor, I'm positive. I got it yesterday, at the pharmacy you told me to—Brewer, Stevens, and Cushing."

Well, then, perhaps Morton was not giving the ether correctly. Probably too much air was inhaled with it. "Do you suppose ether can be kept in a rubber bag?" he asked Hayden the next day.

"I don't know. It might eat the material. Why don't you ask Jackson?"

Clearly Jackson was just the man to answer such

a question. Morton went to see him. He was not sure that it was a good idea, though. Jackson had been acting peculiar lately. He had been making life disagreeable for Samuel F. B. Morse, claiming that he, Charles Thomas Jackson, was the true inventor of the telegraph, since he had explained the whole idea to Morse during an ocean voyage. "If he has any idea what I'm trying to do," Morton thought, "he might push the thing to a quick finish and claim the whole discovery as his own." The dentist would proceed with caution.

Dr. Jackson was working in his laboratory when Morton came in. After making a little conversation, the dentist requested the loan of a gas bag. Jackson located one and said, "Well, Morton, you seem to be all equipped, minus the gas."

"The gas? Oh, yes, well, you see, I have a very nervous patient," Morton said glibly. "If I tell her there's something in the bag to deaden the pain, she might talk herself into it."

Jackson laughed. "That's a silly idea! You'll probably asphyxiate her. Why don't you use ether?"

Morton felt his face grow hot. Ether! Did Jackson really know about ether after all? He grew flustered and stammered some incoherent questions.

"The vapor of ether," Jackson said, "will make people dull and stupefied. Then you can do whatever you want with them and they can't fuss so much."

Ah, so that was all he knew! "Very interesting," Morton said. "I'll try it."

"Get some at Burnett's. Only place in town where they carry a pure grade."

Burnett's was the only place, was it? No wonder the other experiments had failed. The ether was not pure. "Thanks, very much, Doctor. I'll bring the bag back tomorrow."

"You can't put ether in that thing!" Jackson said. "Here—use this." He handed Morton a glass jar with a sponge in it.

Morton hurried to Burnett's pharmacy, bought a bottle of ether, and dashed back to his office. This time, he vowed, he would get some results if he suffocated in the attempt.

He went into the inner room and locked the door. The faint voices of Hayden and the boys in the laboratory made the silence that surrounded him seem lonely and oppressive. Sitting down in the dental chair, he poured some of the ether into the glass jar. The smell of the stuff was overpowering. He pulled a handkerchief out of his pocket and soaked it in ether. Then he looked at his watch, buried his nose in the handkerchief, and inhaled.

After a few seconds he was unconscious.

When he woke up he took a deep breath and looked at his watch. Eight minutes had passed. That split second of blackness during which the world had ceased to exist had really been eight whole minutes!

He rushed into the other room to tell Hayden what had happened. Then he ran home as fast as he could, still so excited that he could hardly speak. But when he told Elizabeth what he had done she was almost as horrified as he was jubilant. "I grew sick at heart," she wrote later, "as the thought came to me that he might have died there alone."

Morton had only one thought. He wanted to do the thing again and at once. He ran back to Tremont Row. This time he would try an extraction. But he could hardly pull his own tooth while he was asleep, and since it was after office hours no patient was likely to appear. Would Hayden care to contribute a tooth to the cause of science? Hayden would not. Well, then, he would take the ether again and Hayden could pull a tooth for him.

He had just begun to inhale when he heard a determined knock on the door. He got up and opened it. A man with a swollen face stood outside. He said, "I have a toothache. Are you still open for—? What's the matter?" For the dentist was beaming at him.

"Nothing. Come right in," said Morton. With great effort he controlled an impulse to dance around the room.

"Now I don't mind telling you I'm scared, Doctor!" said the patient. "I wouldn't have come in here for a hundred dollars if this tooth hadn't been killing me! Could you mesmerize me or something?"

"Mesmerism is no good," Morton said. "I have something much better." He pushed the patient into the chair gently, then poured some ether onto his handkerchief. "If you'll just inhale . . ."

Hayden brought the lamp close to the chair. Morton seized the forceps and closed them over the decaying tooth which the man had pointed out. He pulled. The silence was broken only by the crunch of the roots as they separated reluctantly from the jawbone of Eben Frost, an obscure music teacher whose name would be forgotten today if he had not had a toothache on the night of September 30, 1846.

Eben Frost woke up and looked around, blinking.

Morton said casually, "Are you ready to have the tooth out now?"

Frost steeled himself. "I'm ready," he said.

"Well, it's out already. Look!" Morton triumphantly brandished the forceps which held the tooth.

"No!" Frost leaped from the chair. "No, it can't be! Glory, hallelujah!"

Morton pushed him back into the chair and wiped the blood from his beaming face. He hardly heard the stream of praise that poured from Frost's mouth. "Ether can prevent the pain of having a bad tooth pulled, can it?" he was thinking. "Then it can prevent the pain of any operation in the world."

Dr. Warren had actually agreed. He would try Dr. Morton's "preparation." The surgeon had been doubtful, of course. People were always turning up at the Massachusetts General Hospital and claiming to have discovered pain-killers. But he had finally given way. Two weeks had passed since the interview, and at last a letter had come, inviting Morton to be present at an operation scheduled for ten o'clock on October 16. That gave him exactly twenty-four hours of final preparation. For the first time he was afraid. He would be given only one chance. There could be no question of failure.

At the hospital the next morning Dr. Warren was almost as nervous as Morton. Was it possible, he wondered, that this dentist had really solved the problem of pain in surgery, as he claimed to have done? It was a ridiculous idea, if you thought much about it. Dr. Warren decided that he would not allow himself to hope at all. At ten o'clock he went to the operating room.

The rumor had spread that something different was going to happen. The room was crowded with students and spectators. Dr. Warren came in, looked over the audience, and in the hush inspired by his presence said, "An agent is to be tested this morning for which the amazing claim has been made that it will render the person inhaling it insensible to pain." He looked at the clock that hung over the door. It was five minutes past ten. He said, "We will wait for Dr. Morton."

At a quarter past ten he picked up his scalpel and said in a tone sarcastic enough to hide his disappointment, "Since Dr. Morton has not yet arrived, I presume he is otherwise engaged."

The audience roared with laughter. Exactly at that moment Morton came into the room. He stood in the doorway for a few seconds trying to collect his wits. Then he walked over to the surgeon and said, "I'm sorry, Doctor. The apparatus wasn't quite ready. It—"

"Well, sir," Warren said testily, "your patient is ready."

Morton looked at the man on the operating table, a young painter named Gilbert Abbott. On his neck was the tumor that was to be removed. "Are you afraid?" Morton said softly. "This man," nod-

ding at Frost whom he had brought along for moral
support, "can tell you that you have nothing to
worry about."

Frost would have been delighted to narrate the
events of September 30, of which he was enor-
mously proud. But Abbott said, "I'm not afraid.
I'll do what you tell me."

Morton whispered a few directions, put the mouth-
piece of his cumbersome apparatus to Abbott's
mouth, and turned the valve. The room was still

now. Abbott groaned once and then went to sleep.

The dentist stepped back and bowed to the surgeon. "Dr. Warren," he said, "*your* patient is ready."

Warren again took up his scalpel and went to

work. After the first incision he looked at Abbott's
face. The boy was smiling in his sleep as though
he were dreaming. The surgeon carefully cut away
the growth and his assistants stitched up the wound.
Abbott stirred uneasily and muttered something.

Warren said, "Abbott! Can you hear me?"

"Uh-huh."

"Did you feel any pain?" Warren asked, realiz-
ing how much depended on the answer.

"Pain? Nah. Somebody scratched m'neck. Didn't
hurt." And he went back to sleep.

Still none of the spectators moved. Each of them
had seen the miracle accomplished before his own
eyes, and yet no one could really believe what he
had seen. At last the surgeon turned to the gallery.
What he said was not a beautifully phrased scientific pronouncement, but these are the words for
which we remember John Collins Warren: "Gentlemen, this is no humbug!"

And then the hall came alive. Morton stood and
watched the doctors and students leap to their feet
and cheer him until the glass in the windows rat-
tled. His head was reeling. He could not think
clearly, so he simply muttered half-finished phrases
of thanks to the people who were now shoving each
other out of the way for the chance to shake his
hand.

If at that moment William Morton could have

looked into the future, his triumph would have been tinged with bitterness. For he was standing on the brink of a fierce medical controversy. Charles Thomas Jackson would claim that he and not Morton was the true discoverer of anesthesia. Before the controversy quieted down (it is not really over even today) it had reached the halls of Congress, and by that time a remarkable number of people had decided that *they* were the true discoverers of anesthesia.

But all that was for the future, and nothing dimmed that glorious October 16 of the year 1846. In one day and one hour the history of human suffering had been split into two distinct eras. A gravestone in a Boston cemetery says it all:

WILLIAM T. G. MORTON

Inventor and revealer of anesthetic inhalation,
By whom pain in surgery was averted and annulled;
Before whom surgery was in all times agony,
Since whom science has control of pain.

6

L O U I S P A S T E U R

———————— 1822 – 1895 ————————

The Battle
Against Bacteria

The citizens of Chamonix were accustomed to seeing odd Frenchmen among the tourists who came to explore their glaciers. But on September 21, 1860, the Swiss villagers were treated to an unusual sight. This was the first time they had seen a tourist climb the Alps while carrying thirty-three glass bottles and an alcohol lamp.

It was the mule, of course, who did the actual carrying of the flasks. The Frenchman walked along beside the animal, frowning each time one piece of glassware knocked against another. The guide walked in front, smiling and shrugging at everyone he met as though to say, "Well, I have to make a living!"

The name of the unusual mountain climber was Louis Pasteur. He had gone climbing in the Alps to disprove the doctrine of "spontaneous genera-

tion," a scientific idea that had been widely believed for well over four thousand years.

Louis Pasteur—of all the names in the history of science, this is probably the best known. It is literally a household word, one that we see whenever we read the label on a bottle of milk. The name, in fact, is *so* well known that many people today do not know exactly what it was that Louis Pasteur did to make himself so famous. There is a good reason for this—the very fact that he did so much.

If a man makes a great discovery his name is forever linked to it. Say "Wright brothers" and you think at once of airplanes. Say "Henry Ford" and you think of automobiles. Say "Jenner" and you think of smallpox vaccination, or "Salk" and you think of polio vaccine. Most people, if asked what Louis Pasteur did, would probably say that it had something to do with germs. This is true, but it is only part of the story. The discoveries of Pasteur, and the changes that he made in our lives, are so far-reaching that today we take them for granted. It is hard to realize that one man was responsible for so much well-being.

Pasteur, who was a chemist, influenced the past hundred years of medicine more than any other single individual. The list of his research projects is staggering. There is enough accomplishment in them to win fame for a dozen men. He himself never really believed that he was a profound or original thinker, but in this single case he was wrong. He believed that his success came from hard work, and in this he was partly right. For work he did, tirelessly and methodically, with laboratories and equipment that would make a modern scientist despair.

Pasteur was born in 1822, two days after Christmas, and grew up in Arbois, a little town in eastern France. His father was a tanner of leather. From the day of his birth to the day of his death, Louis Pasteur was blessed in his family life. Without the faith and devotion of his parents, the tanner's son could never have hoped for the kind of education he received. Yet no sacrifice his parents made seemed too hard. They had good reason for their pride in the young Louis.

The letters his father wrote to him during his student days in Paris were far different from most letters to sons away from home, as the elder Pasteur realized. "The presents you sent have just arrived. I shall leave it to your sisters to write their thanks. For my part, I should prefer a thousand times that this money should still be in your purse, and thence to a good restaurant, spent in some good meals that you might have enjoyed with your friends.

There are not many parents, my dearest boy, who have to write such things to their son. My satisfaction in you is deeper indeed than I can express."

Pasteur was twenty-five years old when his name became well known in the scientific circles of Paris for a brilliant piece of research he had done on the formation of tartrate and paratartrate crystals. If he had accomplished nothing more than this and the studies in crystallography that followed, his name would be listed among the great contributors to chemistry and molecular physics. As things turned out, the work was just a promising beginning.

In 1849 Pasteur was appointed professor of chemistry at the University of Strasbourg. The serious young man, so cautious and retiring, had been in town exactly two weeks when he wrote to the Rector of the Strasbourg Academy requesting the hand of his daughter, Marie, in marriage. Marie and her family, who had expected no such results from the courtesy calls of the new professor, naturally had to think it over. The delay before Marie accepted unnerved Pasteur, and he ruefully poked fun at his suddenly changed outlook on life. "I," he wrote, "who did so love my crystals!"

Five years after his marriage to Marie, Pasteur became dean of the newly formed Faculty of Science in the city of Lille. One of the chief industries of the area was the production of alcohol from the fermentation of grain and sugar beet. In the summer of 1856 business was bad. Fermentation was, at best, a tricky process. Sometimes it worked. Sometimes it did not. Since no one knew exactly what caused fermentation in the first place, no one knew how to control it.

Pasteur had a pupil whose father was an important producer of alcohol. This man came to the new dean of science and asked him to investigate the problem of fermentations that went bad. Pasteur was already deeply interested in the theory of fermentation. Now for the first time he was led into a practical concern with this strange phenomenon of nature.

Fermentation is the change brought about in starch and sugar by the action of yeast. It is the process by which bread rises and grape juice becomes wine. In Pasteur's day the most popular explanation of this action was the one given by an important German chemist named Liebig. Briefly, Liebig taught that the ferment—the substance producing the fermentation—was an unstable body in the act of decomposing, or falling apart. This process produced vibrations in the molecules of the ferment, he said, and these vibrations were passed along to the sugar molecules. They, too, began vibrating and thus decomposed into alcohol and carbonic acid, the end products of fermentation.

Pasteur, after a year of painstaking experiments, showed that the ferment, far from being an unstable, dying substance, was very much alive. It did its work by the rapid multiplication of its wildly active cells.

Where did these cells come from, these tiny creatures so powerful that they could change the chemical structure of a molecule? This question led Pasteur to his great work on "spontaneous generation." We have already seen him doggedly climbing the lofty mountain in the pursuit of truth. Few scientists have ever performed a practical task in the line of duty that was at the same time so wonderfully symbolic.

The existence of beings so small that they cannot be seen by the unaided eye had been known for over two hundred years, since the invention of the microscope. They could be seen in a simple drop of water; a piece of old meat or cheese positively swarmed with them. Most people believed that microscopic beings, like yeast cells, were simply formed "spontaneously" by some unknown force which somehow organized them out of the surrounding matter. The air acted as a catalyst—or hastener—in this process. But others, including Pasteur, believed that no living creature, not even the minutest cell of yeast, could come into being unless it was preceded by a parent organism similar to itself.

Pasteur set out to prove that the microscopic creatures found in decomposing matter got into it in the first place from the air, and once there proceeded to multiply.

The flasks that Pasteur carried up the Alps contained an organic liquid in which these creatures were known to form very quickly when in contact with air. The liquid had first been boiled vigorously to kill off any possible life in it. Then it had been sealed up in the flasks, from which all the air had been driven. In other words, it now existed in a vacuum. Pasteur opened the flasks long enough to admit the pure and dustless air of the mountaintop, and then quickly resealed them.

Days passed and weeks passed, but no signs of decomposition appeared. The material in the flask remained as clear and free of microscopic growth as it had been on the day it was sealed in. Yet the same material, when boiled and then exposed in exactly the same way to the air of the city, had quickly spoiled and was soon crawling with microscopic creatures.

Now if these creatures had simply formed themselves spontaneously in the city flasks, they should also have formed in the mountain flasks, since the material in all the flasks was exactly the same. The kind of air admitted should have made no difference.

Pasteur devoted four years of his life to these experiments. Of course they cannot adequately be described in a few paragraphs. But when they were finished, the ancient belief was dead. Nobody believes in spontaneous generation today. Few people remember that it was Louis Pasteur who demolished the doctrine for all time.

Pasteur was essentially a practical man. He was also an ardent patriot. He asked nothing better than to put his scientific genius at the service of his beloved France. No scientist has ever done more for his country than Pasteur, for he literally saved from ruin the two principal industries by which the country lived—the making of wine and the manufacture of silk.

The wine producers were failing because the wine spoiled too soon after bottling, so that it was almost impossible to export it. Pasteur found that the simple process of heating the wine for a short time at about 132° F. would destroy all the organisms that caused spoiling. The process we now call "pasteurization" saved the great wine industry of France and put it on the road to prosperity.

And in the meantime Pasteur had identified and

suggested remedies for the two silkworm diseases that had all but wrecked the silk industry.

In 1868, while he was deep in these labors, Pasteur suffered a severe stroke and nearly died. For a lesser man, this illness and the slight paralysis that followed might have meant the end of active service. But Pasteur was standing on the threshold of more great work.

His studies on fermentation had led him to three conclusions: (1) Ferments are living beings. (2) There is a special, specific ferment for each kind of fermentation. (3) These ferments are not born spontaneously within the fermented matter. They are introduced into it from the outside.

Two hundred years before, a great English chemist named Robert Boyle had made a prophecy. He had said that the man who could probe the secret of fermentation could probably also explain the origin of certain diseases.

During his years of research on fermentation and the diseases of wine, Pasteur had often pondered the question of contagious human diseases, and the possibility that these too had their own specific causes. Gradually the facts were compelling him to a belief that certain diseases are caused because microscopic organisms invade the body.

There was more than pure scientific interest in

his growing concern with this subject. Pasteur, the most tender and devoted of fathers, had buried three daughters, two having died of typhoid fever. "It would indeed be a great thing to give the heart its share in the progress of science," he said. Once he realized that his work might be useful in the battle against human disease, he could not rest, even though he knew what obstacles he would face in proving his theory.

The principal obstacle was the medical profession itself. The doctors of Pasteur's time had their own unshakeable theories on the nature of disease: disease sprang by "morbid spontaneity" from the diseased organism. When a physician named Villemin claimed that tuberculosis is a contagious disease that is passed from one patient to another and cannot be acquired in any other way, his colleagues were outraged. "Tuberculosis," said one of them, neatly summarizing what was generally believed about all diseases, "is the common result of a quantity of different external and internal causes, not the product of a specific agent that is always the same!"

In a hostile, solid rank, the medical men of Paris now closed against this *non*-medical man, a mere chemist, who dared to question their cherished beliefs. They let it be clearly understood that they needed no outsider to tell them how to run their affairs. Let Monsieur Pasteur kindly stay with his work on behalf of French industry, for which they and the rest of the country were eternally grateful. But let him leave the welfare of French medicine in more capable hands.

Pasteur did not even try to make converts among the established members of the profession. It was to the younger generation of doctors—the medical students and recent graduates—that he looked for support. He found it in Doctors Roux, Chamberland, Thuillier, and others whose names became forever linked with his.

Pasteur's battle with the doctors and surgeons of France was at its height when he received a letter from an English surgeon who was practicing in Scotland. The British doctor, Joseph Lister, wrote to say how Pasteur's work had revolutionized his own thinking on surgery and surgical procedure.

Pasteur's own researches in hospital wards and morgues were terribly hard on him, for he was a gentle man who suffered acutely in the presence of suffering. "No one knows," wrote Roux, "what feelings of repulsion Pasteur had to overcome before visiting patients and witnessing post-mortem examinations. . . . The cut of the lancet opening an abscess made him wince as if he himself had received it. . . . We have often seen him go home ill from the operating theaters. But his love of science, his desire for truth were the stronger. He returned the next day."

Of all the hospital diseases he studied, Pasteur fought most bitterly against childbed fever, the deadly infection after childbirth which in some hospitals was claiming as many as 25 out of each 100 patients. Pasteur begged the doctors to use clean linens, to pass instruments through a flame before using them, and especially *not* to go unwashed from a post-mortem dissection to the bedside of a patient. His ideas were met with indifference. One day at the Academy of Medicine an eminent physician was lecturing on the "atmospheric causes" of epidemics in maternity hospitals. Suddenly the irritating Monsieur Pasteur was on his feet, shouting, "None of these things causes the epidemics! It is the nurses and doctors who carry the microbe from an infected woman to a healthy one!"

The speaker, vastly annoyed, peered over his spectacles and said with chill dignity, "I fear that microbe will never be found, Monsieur!"

In reply Pasteur stalked over to the blackboard and drew an ugly, chain-like creature. "There!" he shouted. "This is what it looks like!"

Such outbursts did not increase his popularity in certain medical circles. But in his heart Pasteur knew that he would win. "I shall *force* them to see!

They will have to see!" he said. In the end, of course, they did.

In the laboratory, Pasteur's brilliant work on the development of the anthrax bacillus had proved to all but the hopelessly blind that a specific microbe causes a specific disease. His voyage into "the world of the infinitesimally small" was about to reach its greatest triumph.

In 1880 he began experiments on the bacillus of a fatal animal disease called chicken cholera. The microbe responsible proved to be so vicious that the tiniest drop of a fresh culture on a crumb of bread was enough to kill a healthy chicken. In the course of an ordinary day's work in Pasteur's laboratory, a wonderful thing happened. It was something that happened very seldom in that laboratory.

Somebody made a mistake.

During a routine experiment, a group of chickens were to be given a shot of a fresh culture of cholera germs. By mistake they were injected with culture from an old bottle that had been put away a few weeks before. It had somehow got mixed up with the new bottles before anyone noticed the date on the label.

The hens became ill, but only slightly. In a few days they seemed perfectly well again. It was clear that they had had a very mild case of chicken cholera and had then made a complete recovery.

"In the field of observation," Pasteur had said years before, "chance helps the mind that is prepared." Instead of dismissing the incident as an irritating accident, he now asked himself a historic question. What would happen if these same hens were now shot full of strong, fresh, deadly cholera germs?

What happened was one of the most significant things that has ever happened in the history of medicine: nothing. The hens were unharmed by the deadly dose of fresh cholera germs. Cholera now had no effect on them whatsoever. They had become immune to it, simply by being exposed to its microbes in a weakened and harmless form.

Edward Jenner had never known the principle behind his great discovery of vaccination. He had simply known the results. Pasteur saw clearly that the principle was the same as that of *his* discovery. In honor of Jenner, he too called his method of creating immunity "vaccination." That is why immunizations we receive today are called "vaccinations" although they have nothing to do with cows or cowpox.

Pasteur began experiments in producing vaccines for other diseases. His laboratory had never been in such a state of excitement and enthusiasm, for everybody who worked there realized that what they were doing might well mark a turning point in the battle of mankind against disease. Pasteur began to hope for an opportunity to test his theory on a grand scale and to prove it to the scoffers and skeptics who listened with such amusement to every new paper he read before the Academy of Medicine. The opportunity came much sooner than he really wanted it—in the spring of 1881, just a year after his first accidental immunization. It came not only on a grand scale but on a truly theatrical one.

He had returned to his studies of anthrax, the deadly disease that could sweep through a herd of healthy sheep and wipe it out within a few weeks. In the laboratory, small-scale experiments on an anthrax vaccine were already in progress.

Pasteur's papers on anthrax aroused the wrath of a veterinary named Rossignol. The *Veterinary Press*, of which he was an editor, was widely read and of great influence in a country where sheep-raising was so important. One day Editor Rossignol wrote in his paper: "Will you have some microbes? There are some everywhere! Microbiolatry is the fashion. It reigns undisputed. It is a doctrine which must not even be discussed, especially when its high priest, the learned Monsieur Pasteur, has pronounced the sacred words, *'I have spoken!'* The microbe alone is and shall be the characteristic of a disease. . . . The microbe alone is true, and Pasteur is its prophet!"

Rossignol had a more practical purpose than mere sarcasm. A few months later he demanded a test to prove, or preferably disprove, Pasteur's theory once and for all. Many people believed that Rossignol was pushing the idea of a field trial in order to win fame as the man who unmasked Louis Pasteur as a fraud. Whatever his motives, he made so much noise about his idea that at last the Melun Agricultural Society agreed to finance a full-scale experiment. It offered sixty sheep to be used however Pasteur wanted to use them.

When the offer reached Pasteur, he was delighted and accepted at once. To his wife and his laboratory assistants, all somewhat alarmed, he said, "What has succeeded in the laboratory on fourteen sheep will succeed just as well at Melun on sixty!"

He himself outlined the strict rules by which the game would be played. "We will take the sixty sheep so kindly offered to us," he told his family, "and use them like this. Twenty-five will be given two injections of our weakened culture, twelve or fifteen days apart. Several days later these twenty-five vaccinated sheep will be given a strong dose of the most virulent anthrax culture we can produce. At the same time twenty-five unvaccinated sheep will be given the same dose of the same deadly culture." Then he continued:

"The other ten sheep? We will leave them alone. Then later we can point to our twenty-five vaccinated sheep and say, 'You see? They are just as healthy as these friends of theirs who have never been near a hypodermic needle.'"

"And what percentage of results will we expect?" asked one of his assistants.

Pasteur smiled. "There is only one percentage that matters in this case," he said. "One hundred per cent. The twenty-five unvaccinated sheep must all die of anthrax. The twenty-five vaccinated sheep must all live. We ask for no quarter and we will give none!"

Reading the printed "rules" of the experiment, one of Pasteur's friends said to him, "You remind me of what a general said about Napoleon—that he liked hazardous games with a touch of grandeur and boldness. It was all or nothing with him. You're carrying on in exactly the same way."

"Yes, I am," said Pasteur.

On Sunday, May 5, a crowd of visiting scientists, physicians, veterinarians, newspapermen, and curiosity seekers poured out of the little railroad station at Melun and headed for the farm called Pouilly-le-Fort, where the sixty sheep were waiting. Pasteur and his friends, Doctors Roux, Chamberland, and Thuillier, knew that the majority of the crowd had come to watch the experiment with the firm belief that it would fail. The veterinarians in particular were convinced that no mere chemist from the city had anything to tell them about a disease that they had watched helplessly for years.

But the four friends were outwardly calm. The first injection of the weakened culture into the twenty-five sheep selected for the honor went smoothly and quickly. The second inoculation of the same sheep on May 17 was done as easily. Pasteur wrote to his son-in-law: "On Tuesday, May 31, the third and last inoculation will take place. I feel great confidence. . . . On June 5 at latest the final result will be known, and should be twenty-five survivors out of twenty-five vaccinated. . . . If the success is complete, this will be one of the finest examples of applied sciences in this century."

As the last week passed, excitement grew outside the laboratory as well as inside. On May 31, the largest crowd ever seen in the railroad station of Melun started out for Pouilly-le-Fort.

One of the veterinarians in charge of the experiment suddenly decided that he wanted a triple dose of the deadly vaccine to be given to the fifty sheep. "And shake it up well," a fellow veterinarian suggested, "so that the strong stuff won't all stay at the bottom and be given to the unvaccinated sheep."

"No danger of that," said his friend. "I shall request Monsieur Pasteur to give the injections alternately—first to a vaccinated sheep and then to an unvaccinated sheep."

To all this nonsense, Pasteur said not a word. Whatever foolish request was made he followed without question. He seemed absolutely calm and impassive, almost bored. When it was over he said to the committee, "We shall meet here on June 2 to check the results."

But once he was back in Paris, Pasteur's iron calm began to desert him. At night when he should have been sleeping, unexpected doubts assailed him. Why had he rushed into this experiment so thoughtlessly in the first place? And why had he, of all people, made such hard-and-fast rules by which to judge it? The next day Dr. Roux reported from Pouilly-le-Fort that all the unvaccinated sheep had definite symptoms of anthrax. But so did some of the vaccinated sheep. Three of them had high fevers.

Pasteur's overwrought nerves now gave way completely and he became convinced that he would fail. On the morning of June 2, weary after a sleepless night, he prepared to leave for the station. The doorbell rang, and a telegram was handed to him. It was Madame Pasteur who finally had the courage to open it. "I had a moment's emotion which

made me pass through all the colors of the rain-
bow," she wrote later. But even before she handed
him the message, Pasteur could tell from the look
on her face what the message would say.

He read half-aloud, the words swimming before
his eyes: "Sick sheep among vaccinated lot all completely recovered. Unvaccinated sheep all dead or
dying. Stunning success." It was signed "Rossignol."

The veterinary was no longer sarcastic.

Pasteur's walk from the Melun station to Pouilly-le-Fort was the triumphal march of a hero.

Pasteur's discovery laid the groundwork for a revolution in the history of medicine. From it sprang the new science of immunology, so important in our lives today. Even before Pasteur's death, Roux and his colleagues were at work on diphtheria, the cruel killer of children. Diphtheria research bounced like a tennis ball from France to Germany and back to France, and finally crossed to the United States. Here the Public Health Department of the City of New York added the final touches to the wiping out of the disease.

Today whooping cough, tetanus, diphtheria, and, most recently, polio are diseases against which all children can be protected.

Pasteur himself devised the first of these new vaccines to be used on a human being. In those days the agonizing and deadly disease called rabies, or hydrophobia, was a serious menace. Today we hardly ever think of this disease, except when we take our dogs to the veterinary for their rabies shots.

Hydrophobia lent itself well to Pasteur's experiments because of its very long incubation period. Weeks could pass before the microbe traveled from the bite to the nerve centers that it attacked. This meant that a vaccine given after a bite could still produce immunity before the deadly disease could do its damage.

In March of 1885, Pasteur wrote to a friend: "I have not yet dared to treat human beings after bites from rabid dogs. But the time is not far off, and I am much inclined to begin by myself—inoculating myself with rabies, and then arresting the consequences, for I am beginning to feel very sure of my results." The necessity for this trial on himself was soon dramatically removed. One day in July, an Alsatian boy named Joseph Meister appeared in the laboratory with his mother. The 9-year-old boy had been seriously bitten by a mad dog two days before. Fortunately his doctor had heard of the work that Pasteur was doing, and had urged the child's mother to take Joseph at once to Paris.

Although Pasteur was naturally hesitant about using an untried and possibly dangerous remedy on a human being, there seemed little reason not to do so. The boy was covered with wounds. He was probably doomed to die in any case.

On the advice of two physicians whom he called to examine the boy's wounds, Pasteur immediately had Joseph inoculated. The first inoculation was followed by eleven more, each a little stronger than the one preceding it. During the ten days of the treatment, Pasteur suffered agonies of fear and hope. By day he could not work—a sure sign of mental anguish. By night he dreamed that Joseph Meister was dying, suffocating in the last agonies of the disease.

Yet Joseph Meister did not die. He never developed rabies and was able to return to Alsace.

This was the beginning of still another era in the working life of Pasteur. It was a truly exhausting one. From then on he was deluged with patients from all over the world who had been bitten by rabid animals. The organization set up to handle these cases was the beginning of the famous Pasteur Institute.

Pasteur's health had been failing for some years. In September of 1895 he died, at the age of seventy-two. He was very weak during his last days and could do nothing but sit under the beech trees of the park and listen to the books that his wife and daughters read to him. The last book he asked to hear was a life of St. Vincent de Paul, a great and simple man who had fought so hard to help the sick and the suffering not only of France but of the whole world. Vincent de Paul was Louis Pasteur's favorite saint. The two men had much in common.

7

JOSEPH
LISTER

—————————— 1827 – 1912 ——————————

The Introduction of
Antiseptic Surgery

On the afternoon of December 21, 1846, the distinguished British surgeon, Robert Liston, made his usual dramatic entrance into the operating theater and said, "We are going to try a Yankee dodge, gentlemen, for making men insensible."

The operation that followed was the first in Europe in which surgical anesthesia was used. Among the medical students present that day was a quiet youth named Joseph Lister. As he watched the historic proceedings, the young man realized that surgery was about to enter a new era, an era of such great possibilities that no one could even guess at the extent of them. He decided that he would like to be a surgeon himself, if he proved to have the necessary skill.

Nearly three hundred years before, Ambroise Paré had solved the first great problem of surgeons: the control of bleeding. William Morton, the Yankee dentist, had later come along and solved the second problem: the control of pain. But a third problem remained: the control of the dreaded infection that claimed so many victims after surgery. The unassuming 19-year-old student had no idea who would eventually solve it.

After his graduation from medical school, young Lister, son of indulgent and well-to-do parents, made arrangements for a grand tour of the European Continent. There he planned to study the work of foreign doctors. But since he had one free week before his sailing date, he decided to go up to Scotland for a few days in order to meet Professor James Syme of Edinburgh, whose reputation as a surgeon was world-wide. Once he had met Syme, Lister could see why. He was fascinated by the dour Scot who was said never to waste a word or a drop of blood. It would be well worth it, Lister decided, to postpone his tour for a few weeks and stay in Scotland.

He stayed twenty-four years.

At first he had really believed that Syme was the inducement to delay his trip abroad. But he soon realized that the professor's daughter, Agnes, was a greater one. Shortly after becoming Syme's chief assistant, Joseph Lister became his son-in-law.

The young man was both delighted and surprised by the way his future had arranged itself, for he did not consider himself or his talents to be very special. "I am encouraged to hope," he wrote to his father, "that though I must not expect to be a Liston or a Syme, still I shall get on. Certain it is I love surgery more and more, and this is one great point. . . . As to brilliant talent, I know I do not possess it, but I must try to make up as far as I can by perseverance."

"I love surgery more and more," he had said. But as his practical experience with hospital life grew, he began to wonder why. For hospitals, as Joseph Lister soon realized, were dangerous places, and surgery was a desperate business.

Because of ether and chloroform, speed was no longer the most important factor in an operation. Surgical technique, therefore, was making brilliant advances. But although these methods made fine reading in the medical journals, they did not often do much for the patient. In Lister's own hospital, 43 per cent of surgical cases died. In the Paris hospitals, close to 60 per cent died. In Munich, where 80 per cent of surgical patients died, the town authorities considered burning the hospital to the ground, on the theory that people would be much safer out of it than in it.

The pattern was always the same. Something happened—not during the operation itself, but after the operation. It began with a slight swelling. Inflammation of the wound followed. Then came pus formation, called suppuration, accompanied by a high fever. After that, there was the death certificate to sign. As he signed one certificate after another, Lister asked himself, "Why do so many of them have to die?"

His older and wiser colleagues, as usual, had all the answers. Of course the death of a patient was regrettable and of course young surgeons always took it personally. But what could be done about it? People had to die of something. And certainly the pus formation itself had nothing to do with the cause of death, as young Lister rashly began suggesting. Pus was a good thing, a healthy thing. That was why it was called "laudable pus," praiseworthy pus. It was nature's way of healing a wound "by second intention." The putrefaction of wounds arose within the tissue by spontaneous generation. Surely Lister had learned these simple truths in medical school?

Yes, he had, Lister thought. He had also heard about wounds healing "by first intention," which meant that they healed without benefit of "laudable pus." But not once in his life had he actually seen a hospital wound heal "by first intention." He had begun to grow bitter. How easy it was to cover one's ignorance by the proper choice of words! "Laudable pus . . . first intention . . . second intention . . . spontaneous generation . . ." What did it all mean? To Lister it meant only that his patients died of wound infections. The other doctors could say, if they insisted, that the pus formation in a wound had nothing to do with the patient's death. But Joseph Lister, for all his humility, believed that they were wrong.

The frequency with which the citizens of Edinburgh broke their bones gave him his first clue. Bone fractures are of two kinds: simple and compound. Lister found that for his patients the distinction was one of life and death. In a simple fracture, a bone is broken, is set, is placed in a cast, and is in time as good as new. Lister's patients passed through the ordeal easily, showing no signs of gangrene, septicemia—blood poisoning—or any other disease to which they were exposed. But the compound fractures, Lister noted, were quite another matter. In this type of break, the jagged end of bone pierces the skin and is exposed to the air. Although all his patients with simple fractures recovered, more than half his patients with compound fractures died of one of the plagues so politely called "hospital diseases." From these facts, Lister reasoned—and taught his students—that the infection did not arise "spontaneously" from the tissue itself but was introduced into the wound from the outside. But how?

To the amusement and slight annoyance of his colleagues, Lister began doing some odd things. For example, he washed his hands before an operation as well as after it. Occasionally he even took off his coat and rolled up his sleeves before he started to work. This was not only startling, his older colleagues believed, but even a bit impertinent. The surgeon's black frock coat, after all, was one of his insignia of office, the unofficial uniform of the brotherhood of surgeons the world over. It was worn year in and out until it acquired a crust of dirt and blood of which its owner was often fiercely proud. Through the buttonhole, the surgeon stuck a few strands of silk which he could rip out and use for ligatures when the occasion demanded. And here was young Lister beginning to operate without his coat! Professor Syme's friends hoped that his son-in-law was not going to become eccentric.

In 1860 the Listers moved to Glasgow, where the hospital statistics were even worse than those of Edinburgh. Here too Lister taught his students that the man who learned to control the suppuration of wounds would be one of the greatest benefactors humanity had ever known.

One day he ran into his friend Thomas Anderson, a chemist. "Have you seen any of the papers this French fellow is writing?" Anderson asked. "A chemist chap. What's the man's name—oh yes, Pasteur. Louis Pasteur."

"No, I have never heard of him."

"You must borrow them from me, then. They sound a bit odd, but you talk a bit oddly yourself about some things."

The next day Anderson produced a stack of paperbound pamphlets. Lister, when he had finished his work for the night, settled down in front of the fireplace and began to read.

Pasteur's papers were a revelation to him—the article on wine fermentation, for example. Lister was a wine merchant's son. He had often heard his good Quaker father bewailing the loss of his wine stock because of faulty fermentation. Fermentation was a disease of wine, and this man Pasteur had finally discovered the cause of it. Certain micro-organisms, much too small to be seen with the naked eye, exist in the air, he said. These tiny creatures get into the wine and cause it to spoil. Pasteur went even further than this. He absolutely denied that putrefaction of any kind was caused by "spontaneous generation" or by the action of oxygen. He said that it was caused not by the air itself but by tiny organisms *in* the air.

Lister jumped up and began to pace around the

room. Micro-organisms in the air! A simple fracture heals. A compound fracture does not. What is
the real difference between them? Exposure to the
air.

Of course it was not the air itself that caused the
inflammation and the pus and the gangrene. It
was something *in* the air, something introduced into
the wound from the outside, as Lister had suspected all along. Could these creatures come from
sources other than the air? From the time-honored,
filthy frock coat? From the ligatures dangling from
a buttonhole? From the carelessly washed instruments? From the surgeon's hands?

Lister shuddered. It was really he who was responsible for the death of his patients.

What could he do about this? One cannot perform an operation in a perfect vacuum. There was
no way to exclude air from surgical wounds. But
what about the deadly little organisms? Could they
be excluded? Could they be killed off? How did
one go about killing off something that could not
even be seen?

A visitor from the city of Carlisle told him something odd. The city's sewage system had been
greatly in need of a disinfectant. The authorities
had tried pouring a new German invention, carbolic acid, into the sewers. The smell had disappeared.

"Can you get me some carbolic acid?" Lister asked Anderson.

"German creosote? Stinking stuff, that. Aye, I can let you have some."

On August 12, 1865, an 11-year-old boy named James Greenlees was run over by a cart and carried to the Glasgow Infirmary. When Lister heard that a compound fracture was involved, he ordered a bottle of carbolic acid to be brought to the operating room. Then he went to work.

The boy recovered exactly as though he had had a simple fracture. There was no inflammation, no suppuration, no gangrene or septicemia. Lister said nothing about it to anyone except Agnes and his most trusted assistants. But startling changes were made in the operating room of the Glasgow Infirmary; for now that Lister realized what the acid could do, he began using it on everything that came in contact with the patients. The bandages, instruments, and ligatures were steeped in it. Even the air in which he worked was sprayed with it by means of a complicated apparatus (actually unnecessary, as we now know), which his students named the "donkey engine." The surgeon's frock coat was thrown out and replaced by a white apron. The water in which he and his assistants scrubbed their hands was mixed with the acid.

For almost a year Lister worked out the theory

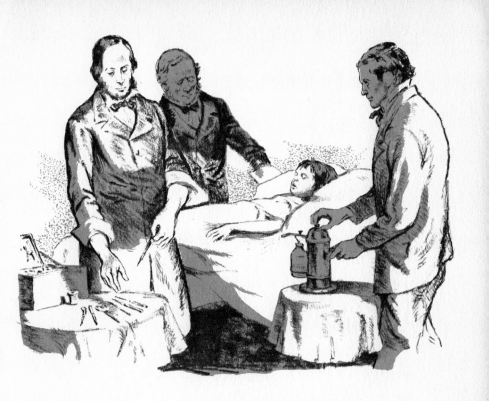

and the practice of his method, watching and re-
cording the history of each case until he had built
up a body of proof that left no doubt in his mind.
His wards reeked of carbolic fumes, but the smell
of decay and death had disappeared.

On March 16, 1867, the physicians and surgeons
of England opened their weekly medical journal,
The Lancet, and read a paper called "On a New
Method of Treating Compound Fractures, Abscesses,
etc., with Observations on the Conditions of Suppuration." Most of the doctors gave a mental shrug
of the shoulders and turned to the next article.
The press complicated matters by announcing that

Mr. Lister of Glasgow had discovered carbolic acid or thought he had.

The idea of antisepsis—for which carbolic acid was only one of several possible agents—escaped most of the doctors who read Lister's paper. A few surgeons tried his methods without really understanding them. Their bungling only made matters worse. Following the lead of the press, these men assumed that the carbolic acid itself had some unusual power. They sprinkled it sparingly around the operating room, and then made their incisions with dirty instruments and dirty hands. When their patients continued to die, they abused Lister fluently.

But for Joseph and Agnes Lister, who had returned to Edinburgh, the next eight years were happy ones. They learned to ignore the controversy that raged around them. The work that Lister was doing down the street was much more important to them than complaints from the rest of the world. Since they could see the results of his work by walking through the local hospital, they bided their time and ignored the latest "refutation" in *The Lancet*. The case notes dictated to Agnes at the end of her husband's long day were growing fat with the history of successful operations.

There was one aspect of the controversy that was hard to endure. Lister's own colleagues at the Edinburgh Hospital refused to have anything to do with his methods. Yet the contrast between his wards and their wards was as clear-cut as the contrast between the smell of antiseptics and the smell of decaying flesh. Yes, the other surgeons of Edinburgh admitted, there was clearly a difference between their wards and Lister's. Their patients still died of hospital diseases and his did not. But to attribute this difference to a swarm of mythical fungi which Lister claimed he could kill off with that reeking acid of his—well, as men of integrity they could simply not go along. It was somehow unprofessional. For that matter, so many things about Lister were slightly unprofessional.

This man, this distinguished surgeon who should know better, visited his patients every day to ask them how they felt and to change their bandages himself. What did the man have assistants for? What was worse, he always ended his visits by tucking in their bedclothes and offering to bring them another blanket or a hot water bottle—himself! And fancy the professor of surgery of the University of Edinburgh sitting on the bed of an 8-year-old girl, sewing the leg of a rag doll! Was this sort of thing good for hospital discipline? Did it not somehow lessen the holy awe and respect in which patients should hold their doctors?

While his colleagues fretted over him, Lister went on his gentle, unconcerned way, saving his patients' lives and trying to cheer them up while doing so. And over the years he continued making improvements in the techniques of surgery—improvements that benefit us today.

The most commonplace of his inventions is the use of the catgut ligature. During his early days as a surgeon, silk ligatures were used. Their ends were

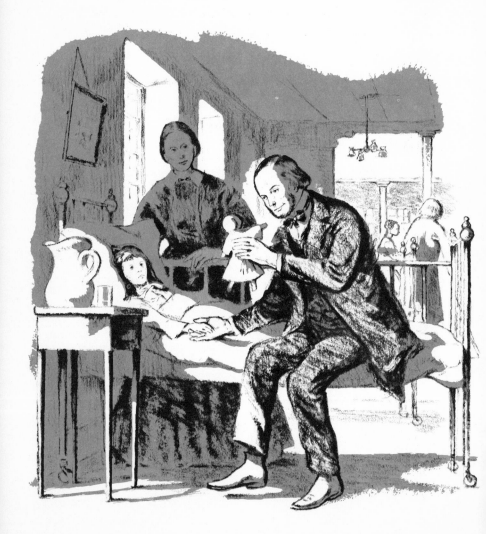

left dangling from the wound until such time as the surgeon felt they could be pulled out without causing more than a mild hemorrhage. Neither the material nor the system was satisfactory.

Lister knew that the human body is remarkably able to absorb foreign particles into itself, as long as the foreign particles are not sources of infection. He wondered whether antiseptic silk might be absorbed in time, without doing any permanent damage.

In December of 1867, he made his first experiment. The patient was an old and ailing horse. Lister cut open the horse's neck and tied a silk ligature around an artery. Then he sewed up the opening and waited. In due time the horse recovered, with no ill effects. Ungraciously he then waited to die of old age until one stormy night when Lister was in bed with the flu. Between sneezes Lister again opened up the horse. By the light of the stable lantern he saw what he had hoped to see: the silk had been neatly walled off by the surrounding tissue. Now he knew that it was no longer necessary to remove the ligatures used inside the body.

To find a material stronger than silk, he experimented for over a year on various animal materials, including kangaroo tails. Finally he opened one of his lectures by saying, with the faint stammer

that always showed up in moments of stress, "Cat-gut, gentlemen, comes not from the cat but from the sheep." This was the first mention of a hospital material as familiar today as adjustable beds.

Although British doctors remained stubbornly cool to Lister's ideas, doctors from abroad were eager to find out just what was going on in this Edinburgh ward, where surgical patients did not die of infections. The hospital swarmed with Germans and Frenchmen, with Danes and Italians and Americans. The visitors carried Lister's methods home with them. In 1875 they persuaded him to return their calls, to see how the rest of the world regarded his work. The man whose countrymen snubbed his methods found himself a hero on the Continent. His tour across Europe was a triumph. Munich welcomed him with the most heartfelt ovation of all; for its mortality rate of 80 per cent among surgical patients had dropped to zero. In Boston, the students at the Harvard Medical School, after watching Lister perform an operation, stood up and cheered.

At home things were much the same. When Lister in 1877 reluctantly accepted the professorship of surgery at King's College in London, he was received with suspicion and open unfriendliness. London was not so naïve as Edinburgh, his colleagues hinted. Just because a man had operated on the Queen, London surgeons would not automatically accept his odd notions. Naturally, more of his surgical patients lived today than had lived twenty years earlier. Hospitals were simply better-run and better-built places, since the strong-minded Florence Nightingale had taken up the battle for hospital reform.

But gradually even the English doctors were forced to believe. In 1878 a young German named

Robert Koch published a book on the causes of wound infection. He proved to a heartening number of people, even the most stubborn, that Lister's "mythical fungi" were perhaps not so mythical after all. Germany was also the source of a new method called asepsis. It is used today. The German surgeons used boiling water instead of the unpleasant carbolic acid to kill off germs. As Lister had said, it was not the presence of the acid that mattered; it was the absence of the bacteria.

Joseph Lister lived out his old age in an aura of peace and glory. The honors and titles heaped on him by foreign governments, and at last by his own, were tokens of the world's gratitude. The world is always grateful in time. Lister lived long enough to be thanked in person. He died in 1912, but long before that he had become a living legend.

On December 27, 1892, Louis Pasteur was seventy years old, and from every corner of the world men gathered in Paris to honor him. From London came Lister. Because Pasteur was too weak to read his address to the visitors, it was read by his son.

"Young men, young men," Pasteur had written at the end of the address, "whatever your profession may be, do not let yourself be touched by barren skepticism, nor discouraged by the sorrows of certain hours that pass over a nation. Live in the serene peace of your laboratories and your libraries. Say first: 'What have I done for my own instruction?' Then, as you go further, 'What have I done for my country?'—until that moment when you shall have, perhaps, the tremendous happiness of thinking that you have contributed in some little way to the progress and good of humanity. But whatever favors life may give or refuse to a man's work, he ought, as he draws near the end of it, to have the right to say, 'I have done what I could.'"

And Lister rose and stretched out his arms to embrace Pasteur.

Louis Pasteur has rightly been called "the most perfect man ever to enter the kingdom of science." Few other men of the kingdom of science approach that description as nearly as Joseph Lister.

There were those in the audience who said that the sight of the two great ones in each other's arms was a symbol of the common brotherhood of science. It is more likely that Lister embraced his master because he, more than any other man in the room, understood what Pasteur was trying to say.

8

ROBERT
KOCH

———————— 1843 – 1910 ————————

The Search
for Disease Germs

Pasteur's discoveries had uncovered a vast new
realm of knowledge, and all over the world scientists began exploring it. Of all the questions raised
by his work, the crucial one was this: are microbes
really a cause of disease?

Pasteur and his followers were passionately convinced that they were. But this did not mean that
everyone agreed with them. As of the year 1876,
no one had yet succeeded in proving to the satisfaction of everyone else that the germ theory of
disease was true beyond a shadow of anyone's
doubt. There was a good reason for this. No one
had yet followed the life cycle of a specific microbe
and proved that it caused a specific disease.

The careful German scientists, in particular, distrusted what they considered the hit-or-miss methods of French research. Professor Cohn, the distinguished head of the Botanical Institute at Breslau, for example . . . Few men knew more about bacteria than Professor Ferdinand Cohn, but no one was going to make Professor Cohn leap to any conclusions about them. What was needed, the professor said, was one perfect piece of laboratory research to show that bacteria truly live, multiply, work, and die in an orderly way, as other plants and animals do. Where would it come from? Well, the professor thought, the finest laboratory talent in the world was gathered under one roof right here in Breslau. Perhaps some day . . .

Many miles away, in a little Silesian village, the wife of a district health officer was worrying over a problem that seemed, on the surface, remote from the academic problems of the learned scientists.

Her husband, Robert Koch, wanted a microscope that he could not afford. Emmy determined that he was going to have it. She economized heroically. On his twenty-eighth birthday she presented him with the microscope. Koch carried the precious gift into his office, strung a sheet across the middle of the room, and said, "There! From now on the outside half is consulting room and the inside half is laboratory!"

Koch was a restless young man. Within the past

five years he had tried practicing medicine in five different towns, and he had not been happy in any one of them. He had not been cut out for the life of a country doctor.

Since the age of five Robert Koch had planned to become an explorer. The ambition never left him. In boyhood, his greatest joy came from wandering in the mountains of his birthplace, investigating the mosses and lichen that clung to the ancient trees, or studying the creatures that lived in the mountain pools. In those days his greatest treasure was a magnifying glass.

His father, a poor miner, wanted to apprentice the boy to a shoemaker. Young Robert, however, dreamed of studying medicine and becoming ship's doctor on voyages of exploration to unknown places. But when he had finally worked his way through the medical school of the University of Göttingen, the problem of his future did not seem so simple and clear-cut as it once had.

How exactly did one go about living a life of adventure? He considered becoming a military surgeon, until he realized that the German army had no use for a surgeon as near-sighted as Robert Koch. He dreamed of emigrating to America, where he understood that fortunes could be made with ease. He took an ill-paid job in a Hamburg hospital because Hamburg was the great port of embarkation, where he could keep an eye on the shipping news.

But there was Emmy to be considered. He had known Emmy Fraatz nearly all his life. They had played together as children. By the time he became engaged to her, he should have known her well enough to realize that a life of adventure on the high seas was not exactly what Emmy had in mind. So Robert Koch ended up as a country doctor, which was not exactly what *he* had had in mind.

The Kochs drifted from one depressing post to another. They came at last to Posen, a small congenial town in the province of Wollstein, in East Prussia. In addition to his own practice, Koch became district health officer, in charge of vaccinating the population and reporting to the government on epidemics of anthrax and other common diseases of country life.

Like many young doctors, Robert Koch was profoundly stirred by the arguments over microbes now raging in the medical journals. When he settled in Posen, he had had his microscope for just two months. Koch determined to put it to real use by investigating the elusive microbes for himself.

One of the diseases under serious discussion at the time was anthrax. (This was several years before Pasteur's development of the anthrax vaccine.)

Davaine, a disciple of Pasteur, had claimed that anthrax was caused by a microbe, but he had not been able to trace its development. Koch knew that if such a thing as an anthrax-causing microbe existed, he should be able to find it in Posen. Wollstein was grazing country. On his evening rounds he was just as likely to find a farmer's wife weeping for a dead sheep as for a sick child. Anthrax was the deadliest of all animal diseases, in Germany as well as France. Koch had seen many sheep-shearers, as well as sheep, succumb to the disease.

He settled a cageful of mice in a corner of his laboratory and went to work. Drawing some blood from an anthrax-stricken sheep, he injected it into the first mouse. In due course the mouse showed symptoms of anthrax and died. This was interesting but proved absolutely nothing. A second mouse, injected with blood taken from the first mouse, also died. So did a third mouse, injected with blood taken from the second mouse. In thirty days an unbroken chain of thirty mice had passed the disease along to one another. Here was proof enough for anyone that something in the blood stream of anthrax victims was capable of passing on the disease. Something—but what?

Koch's microscope showed him that anthrax blood swarms with little rods and dots and threads. These bodies he could not find in healthy blood, no matter how many specimens of it he examined. Wasn't this proof, Emmy asked, that the rods and threads were the causes of anthrax?

Not at all, Koch replied. It was just as possible that these scraps in the blood were simply disorganized matter, formed there as a result of the disease. There was only one way to prove that they were the cause of anthrax and not its effect. He would have to isolate a pure strain of them in a test tube. From this strain alone he would have to produce the disease in the thirty-first mouse.

At times Emmy regretted the purchase of the birthday present. No woman, she thought, had ever had such a time-consuming rival. About three sentences a day was all she ever heard from her husband now. The work begun as an interesting diversion had taken hold of him completely.

Koch invited another doctor to take over most of his private practice, so that he could devote himself to his research. But there was an even surer sign that the work had become an obsession. Robert Koch, former chess champion of the University of Göttingen, gave up his nightly chess game.

How was he to isolate a pure strain of the microbe? How could he grow a colony of anthrax bacilli—if they existed—that had never been inside the body of an anthrax victim?

After many false starts, Koch invented a marvelous method of doing this. He placed a drop of the clear liquid from an ox's eye on a thin glass slide. Into the liquid he dropped a tiny piece of tissue snipped from a dead mouse. Then he took a thicker slide and scooped a little well out of its center. He placed the thick slide over the thin slide and turned the whole thing upside down. He now had an airtight "hanging drop" of liquid. Nothing could get in and nothing could get out. Placing the slide on the stage of his carefully warmed microscope, he waited, his eye glued to the eyepiece. Minutes stretched into half an hour. The half-hour dragged out into an hour. Not until two hours had passed did anything begin to happen. Then at last the little rods and threads of the anthrax tissue began to divide and grow and stretch themselves out. After three hours the slide was covered with a tangled mass of them, more than Koch had ever seen at once.

He opened the slide and extracted a tiny drop of liquid, about the size of a pinhead. This he placed in a second "hanging drop" of ox-eye liquid, exactly like the first. The rods and threads began growing rapidly, filling every available corner of the drop with their long tendrils. Koch repeated the process six times. The creatures on the eighth slide, he knew, were only distantly related to the original material from the sick mouse. Whole generations of life separated them.

Were these energetic creatures alive? Definitely so. He had seen them grow and reproduce themselves, the two commonplace activities of living things. There was abundant life on the slide. But was this life capable of destroying other life?

He took one drop of culture from the eighth slide and injected it into a mouse. The next morning the mouse was dead. Its body was swarming with bacilli, and from some of these he again grew a pure culture of the same microbes.

The germ theory of disease was no longer a theory. It had become a fact overnight—even though no one else knew it.

One question remained. The same loophole had perplexed Davaine and other investigators of anthrax. Koch now faced up to it himself. These bacilli were delicate creatures. They dried up and died in two days, even in the warmth of the laboratory. How could they live, in the frozen fields of Posen, winter after winter, returning each spring full of vigor and able to infest whole herds of sheep and cattle?

Certain of his cultures had shown black dots, stringing across the slide like black beads. Koch had assumed that these were broken fragments of the threads. But now he remembered the little black dots. He also remembered that no scientist has a right to assume anything he has not proved.

He allowed a culture that showed the black dots to dry up and die. Then he poured some fresh, warm ox-eye fluid onto the slide. As he watched through the microscope, the tiny dots—spores, he called them—burst open and sprouted into full-grown anthrax bacilli. So that was it! That was why the soil of a field could be polluted with anthrax for year after year. The little bacilli were not so delicate after all. In winter they hibernated. In spring they blossomed out again, all ready to get back to work. From spore to full-grown bacillus and back again to spore; from the body of a dead sheep to the blood of a living sheep; from that doomed sheep to another living sheep—it was an endless cycle of destructive life.

On April 22, 1876, Professor Cohn of Breslau received a letter in the morning mail.

Esteemed Herr Professor:

Stimulated by your work on bacteria published in *Contributions to Plant Biology,* I have for some time been at work on investigations of anthrax contagion. . . . After many vain attempts I have finally been successful in discovering the process of development of the *bacillus anthracis.* . . . I would therefore respectfully request you to permit me to show you, within a few days, in the Botanical Institute, the essential experiments. . . .

Yours respectfully,
R. KOCH, District Physician

"The process of development of the bacillus." Who was this "R. Koch, District Physician," who claimed to have done something that men such as Ferdinand Cohn had not yet managed to do? Professor Cohn was getting tired of these amateurs who kept turning up and claiming to have solved this or that complex problem in bacteriology. But, since he was a fair-minded man, he invited the country doctor to come to the Institute and perform. He even provided him with a distinguished audience of scientists.

The demonstration, given on three successive days, was a theatrical success. Everything went off exactly on cue. Spores grew, bacilli multiplied, mice died like seasoned troupers. At last Koch peered at the company through his gold-rimmed spectacles and said, "Well, gentlemen, I believe that concludes the demonstration." No one moved at first. Then Dr. Cohnheim, one of the most venerable of the spectators, leaped to his feet and rushed down the hall, his coattails flying out behind him. He dashed into his own laboratory and shouted to his assistants, "Go at once to Koch! The man's discovery is the greatest ever made with bacteria! He leaves nothing to be proved!" As the surprised young men rushed out the door, he looked around the well-equipped laboratory. "Way out in the country," he muttered, shaking his head, "and all alone! We ought to be ashamed of ourselves!"

No one who loved science could really be jealous. Eventually the German government, too, began to be impressed by Robert Koch, for the eyes of the world were soon turned on him. Could such a man be left to work in a sheep-raising town in Wollstein? Certainly not. Governments do not like to be rushed, however, and it took Professor Cohn and the others four years to arrange for Koch's transfer to Berlin.

Here, at last, he was established in a well-equipped laboratory in the Imperial Health Bureau. Here he made the brilliant experiments in solid-culture media on which the new science of bacteriology would flourish.

The great microbe hunt was on. Within the next few years investigators—spurred by rivalry between French and German scientists—identified the bacilli of leprosy, typhoid, pneumonia, tetanus, meningitis, syphilis, diphtheria, and many others. But there was one disease in particular on which Robert Koch had his eye, and in 1881 he muttered to himself the scientific German equivalent of, "Stand aside, boys! This one's mine!"

After Jenner's conquest of smallpox, tuberculosis had taken its place as the world's most dangerous disease. One out of every seven people were doomed to die of it, while the most skillful doctors in the world stood by helpless. Theories about tuberculosis were still split between the disciples of Laënnec and those of Broussais. The latter scoffed at the idea that tuberculosis was caused by a bacillus. Ridiculous! It was not even contagious. But Laënnec had always believed in a "specific agent." So had Villemin. So also did Robert Koch.

All that Koch would accept as a fact, however, was the contagiousness of the disease. He had only an instinctive feeling that there was really a bacillus somewhere. Other diseases had readily yielded up their bacilli. He had never seen anything that could remotely be suspected of being a tuberculosis bacillus. But if one existed, he determined, then he would find it. Early in August of 1881 he began the search.

He himself had already mapped the procedure. In his first publication—the paper on anthrax—he had stated the famous "four postulates," or rules, which have been followed ever since: (1) Find the suspected microbe in every case of the disease. (2) Isolate a pure strain of it outside the body. (3) With this strain alone, produce the disease in a laboratory animal. (4) From the body of the victim, recover the microbe and grow it again.

The first step, then, was to find something that looked like a bacillus and that occurred again and again in tuberculous tissue. Material with which to work was all too plentiful. Berlin hospitals were full of patients dying of tuberculosis.

Robert Koch was feeling his way through the dark. There were no rules to follow, except the hard rules he had made himself. There were no teachers to advise him and no techniques to copy. He invented them as he went along.

The work did not go well. Koch's laboratory associates, Gaffky and Löffler, rarely arrived in the morning without finding him already bent over the microscope, his hands brightly colored by whatever stain he had been trying the most recently. To detect the elusive bacillus, he had tried every type of stain known to the laboratory. He had invented his own stains and combinations of stains, but still there was nothing on any of his slides that could pass for a bacillus.

Thus matters stood for some weeks. His carefully kept notebooks showed him that he had searched over two hundred slides of material that should have been crawling with tuberculosis bacilli—if there were such things.

One day he tried a stain that had first been used by a colleague named Paul Ehrlich: a weak solution of the dye called methylene blue. Twenty-four hours later, when Koch washed the stained slide and put it on his microscope, he thought that he saw slender blue rods, faintly outlined against the blue slide. They certainly looked like bacilli, but not exactly like any bacillus that he had ever seen. Koch refused to leap to the conclusion that he, first of all men, had finally seen the most destructive creature in the world.

How could he make the blue rods stand out more clearly? Koch was a pioneer in the brand-new technique of photographing microbes. He decided to try the kind of color combination that worked well in photography. First he would add the methylene blue to the slide, to stain the bacilli. Then he would add a brown stain to the slide to provide a background. Now at last the little blue rods stood out as unmistakable microbes. Were they the bacilli of tuberculosis? Perhaps. But he had a long way to go before he could give a definite answer.

Greatly encouraged, he now opened a fresh bottle of methylene blue and made up a fresh supply of slides, all presumably covered with tuberculosis bacilli. But he could find nothing on any one of them that even faintly resembled the original blue rods. What had happened to them? Where had they gone?

Koch consulted Löffler and Gaffky. For days the three men went over every step of the laborious process, trying to figure out what had gone wrong. At last they had it. The first bottle of methylene blue had been standing around the lab for some time. It had picked up enough ammonia from the atmosphere to become slightly alkaline. The new, fresh bottle, specially made for the occasion, was *not* alkaline. That small bit af alkalinity made all the difference.

Koch made a new set of slides. This time he added a drop of potassium hydroxide to the methylene-blue solution. The blue rods reappeared, more easily visible than before. He had at last hit upon the exact conditions they demanded in order to show themselves.

Now Koch could really get to work. Now he would track down the temperamental creature in every case of tuberculosis in Berlin, if necessary, to prove that it truly existed in every case.

The blue rods turned up on hundreds of slides. Koch found them in lung tissue, in bronchial glands, in kidneys, in skin lesions, in diseased bone.

He found them in tuberculous sheep and pigs and goats and chickens. He was by now ready to admit that they were connected in some way with tuberculosis.

Koch prepared to move along to the second stage of his procedure. Now he had to make the elusive creature grow on its own in a test tube.

Within a few days he was again in the depths of gloom. The little rods positively refused to grow in any one of the tempting, well-tested media he prepared for them. The most lovingly cooked gelatins failed to please them. After several weeks of disheartening trial and error, he had a new idea. Since the bacillus was too sensitive to grow outside the body, he would pamper it by producing, as nearly as he could, the exact conditions it found inside the body. He purified some cow's blood, hardened it to a firm jelly, and planted in it a snip of tissue from a tuberculous guinea pig. Then he placed the tube in an incubator, warmed to the exact body temperature of the animal, and waited.

Days passed while absolutely nothing happened inside the tube. A week passed, and then another week. No bacillus in the world would take this long to grow. Clearly the blue rods were not really tuberculosis bacilli after all. Probably there was no such thing as a tuberculosis bacillus. Or, if there was, then someone else would have to find it.

But Koch did not throw away the tube. And at the end of the second week, as he pulled it out of the incubator, it seemed to him that the surface was not quite as smooth as it had been the day before. He squinted his near-sighted eyes and looked again. Surely it was different! He seized a magnifying glass and carried the tube over to the light. He was right! The surface of the jelly was covered with a fine growth.

Koch seized a slide and transferred a tiny particle of the fuzz from the tube. Then he stained the slide. The blue rods were there, as he had known in his cautious heart that they had to be.

"Now!" he said to Löffler and Gaffky, after they too had looked, and rejoiced, and pumped his hand. "Now, I *really* get to work! I want the healthiest guinea pigs in Berlin. And a rabbit and a cat and—do you suppose I could get hold of a donkey?"

Cultures grown from the tube were injected into 217 laboratory animals. All 217 died of tuberculosis. In their bodies Koch found and grew the pale-blue bacillus.

He had followed every step of his own rules.

The evening of March 24, 1882, was cold and rainy. The meeting of the Berlin Physiological So-

ciety was crowded but not congenial. The pro-bacillus men sat on one side of the room. The anti-bacillus men sat on the other.

Koch said nothing to anyone, but wondered how he could possibly speak when his throat was so

dry. The meeting was called to order. He looked at the audience over the rim of his glasses and then began to read in a shaking voice: "On the Etiology of Tuberculosis."

"That evening remains graven in my mind," Paul

Ehrlich wrote later, "as the most majestic scientific event in which I have ever participated."

When Koch sat down and the chairman called for questions or objections, not a man in the room opened his mouth. The paper required no questions and permitted no objections.

The significance of what Koch had proved must have been clear to most people in the audience even before he finished reading. Tuberculosis was not a degenerative disease that developed haphazardly within the body. From now on all research on its prevention and cure would spring from this discovery. The deadly disease was caused by a bacillus, which was passed from one victim to the next. The control of that process was now one of the supreme responsibilities of every government, every public health department, and every obscure district physician in the world.

9

FREDERICK BANTING

——————— 1891 – 1941 ———————

The Control
of Diabetes

Dr. Frederick Grant Banting, an instructor in physiology at the University of Western Ontario, did most of his class preparation during his evening office hours. He had found that this was a most convenient time to work. He was sure to be alone.

After studying at the University of Toronto, the young Canadian had come to London, Ontario, to practice orthopedic surgery. After twelve weeks he found that he was averaging four dollars a month in fees. He was a good surgeon, but he was a new surgeon. The citizens of London, Ontario, took their broken bones elsewhere, and Dr. Banting began to look for an extra job.

He was already teaching one course in surgery at the university. One day he heard that the department of physiology needed an extra instructor to take over a new section of sophomores. Banting went in to the head of the department and carefully explained that he was not really a physiologist, had done no post-graduate work in the subject, and in fact had given it no serious thought since leaving medical school. Then he asked for the job. He was hired on the spot. The head of the department, repaying honesty with honesty, admitted that Banting was being given the extra class because no one else had applied for it.

In this most casual way, Frederick Banting entered the field of physiology.

In addition to being an extremely honest young man, Banting was conscientious. He took his new job seriously. He determined to keep more than one chapter ahead of the class. This was why he studied physiology during the quiet hours of the evening, when he was supposed to be seeing patients.

Every night he carried home a stack of books and journals from the university library. The mysteries of the human body in action began to fascinate him. He wondered whether he had not made a mistake in adopting surgery as a specialty.

One night, late in October of 1920, he began preparing material for the next week's lectures: the effect of the pancreas on carbohydrate metabolism. Carbohydrate metabolism is the process by which the body uses starch and sugar to produce energy.

Banting's textbook was open to a diagram of the digestive organs. He glanced at the small, oblong organ lying behind the stomach—the pancreas. This organ has two kinds of cells: outer cells and inner cells.

The outer cells of the pancreas produce three strong digestive juices, called enzymes. Ducts carry the enzymes from the outer cells to the digestive tract. When carbohydrate reaches the intestine, the digestive juices go to work on it and change it to glucose. The glucose is picked up by the blood stream and carried to the liver. There it is changed to glycogen, which is stored until it is needed.

Whenever the body needs energy—enough to breathe or enough to hit a home run—a remarkable series of events takes place. Glycogen is sent from the liver to the muscle. Here it is changed back into glucose. The glucose then unites with oxygen from the lungs and is burned. The result? Energy.

The inner cells of the pancreas also play a vital role in this process. A secretion from the inner cells promotes both the forming and the storing of glycogen. When the glycogen is changed back to glucose, the inner pancreatic secretion is the "spark" that sets off its burning with oxygen. If for any reason the secretion fails to arrive—if the pancreas is injured or for some reason is not producing the secretion—then the "unsparked" sugar accumulates, first in the muscle, then in the blood. Then the patient's reserves of energy are gone and soon he is dying. He is dying of diabetes.

The subject of diabetes did not properly belong to the sophomore physiology class. But once it had been called to mind by his reading, Banting could not immediately put it out. He had held a personal grudge against diabetes since the day a dear childhood friend had died of it.

There was no way his friend could have been saved. No child with diabetes ever lived longer than a year at the most. For in 1920 diabetes was an incurable disease. It could be treated by one method only—heroic dieting, almost starvation. The physician of the day dreaded the disease almost as much as his patients did. It was a cruel illness to treat and a terrible one to die of.

In the wave of brilliant research that followed the discoveries of Pasteur and Koch, diabetes had no part. Here there was no germ to look for, no vaccine to develop, no contagion to check. Diabetes does not come from the outside. It comes because a delicate mechanism inside the body breaks down.

The pancreas was not known to be connected with diabetes until 1888, when German scientists proved it beyond doubt. Their method was simple enough. They removed the pancreases of laboratory animals, and found that without exception diabetes resulted. Dr. Friedrich Naunyn and his colleagues also found that the enzymes from the outer cells of the pancreas had no connection with the disease. One could tie the ducts of these outer cells and cut off the flow of the enzymes without producing a single symptom of diabetes. It was the inner cells that mattered.

Twenty years before Naunyn's discoveries, another German named Paul Langerhans had first discovered these inner cells that poured their secretion directly into the blood stream. When Naunyn's discovery was added to that of Langerhans, the two interlocked neatly. Diabetes was caused by the failure of these inner cells—the "islets of Langerhans"—to secrete their mysterious substance.

Banting could predict a question that his students would ask him. If diabetes is caused by a lack of this secretion, then why not simply extract it from animal pancreases and supply it to the patient artificially?

So obvious an idea had, of course, been thought of. But there was a catch to it. There were, in fact, three catches—the three digestive juices. These enzymes are powerful chemicals. Brought into contact with the delicate secretion of the inner cells, they destroy it. One could take out an animal pancreas, grind it up, make a solution of its "extracts," and inject the solution into a diabetic patient. There would be two results. The patient would be supplied with a quite unnecessary dose of enzymes, and these strong secretions would give him a skin boil.

Banting was vaguely aware that many distinguished researchers had given their best efforts to this particular problem. It was not likely that a poorly prepared instructor in sophomore physiology could do anything about it, no matter how much time he spent preparing for his classes. The following week he gave what he considered an inadequate lecture on the pancreas, and left it at that.

The subject came up again quite by chance. One afternoon the librarian handed him a new issue of a surgical journal and offered to let him borrow it overnight. Banting tucked the magazine under his arm and went home. That evening, after he had finished preparing the next day's class, he opened the journal to the first article. "The Relation of the Islets of Langerhans to Diabetes," it was called, with the typical longwindedness of scientific titles, "with Special Reference to Causes of Pancreatic Lithiasis." It was by Dr. Moses Barron of Minneapolis.

Banting was surprised to find his favorite subject turning up in a journal of surgery. He knew the reputation of the author. Dr. Barron was an authority in lithiasis—stone formation within the body. His article described some strange cases that had come to his attention. Pancreatic stones had lodged not in the pancreas itself but in the ducts connecting its outer cells to the intestinal tract. In every case, he reported, the blocking off of these pancreatic ducts had been followed by a destruction of the external cells. The strong digestive juices, unable to escape, had turned themselves against the very cells that produced them. Eventually the cells were destroyed.

Banting mused over the article for the rest of the evening. Then he went upstairs to bed and fell asleep—or almost. At the boundary of consciousness he suddenly jumped out of bed, rushed over to the desk, and wrote himself a note. Then he went back to bed, still half asleep.

When he woke up the next morning, he studied his note thoughtfully. "Ligate the pancreatic ducts of dogs," he had written. "Wait six to eight weeks for degeneration. Remove the residue and extract." That was all. But why had such a simple procedure not been carried out long ago? He sat down at his desk and continued to stare at the piece of paper. Where were the errors in his reasoning? Where was the flaw in the method? If you tied off the ducts of the outer cells of the pancreas, you could make them dry up completely, just as they dried up when accidentally blocked off by stones. Substitute string for stones and you would get the same results. Then, if the outer cells were dried up, they could hardly go on secreting the strong digestive juices, could they? And if the strong digestive juices were no longer in the pancreas, what would be left but the internal cells and their pure secretion?

As far as Frederick Banting could determine, the only thing wrong with the method was that no one —as far as he knew—had ever tried it. He went to the head of the physiology department and told him the story. The doctor was naturally surprised to find his young assistant eager to plunge into the most complicated kind of physiological research, but he was impressed. It was a promising research project, he told Banting. It deserved better facilities than the small laboratory of the university. "Go to the University of Toronto," he told the young man. "There's a man there who should hear about this—Professor Macleod. His lab is the place for you to work."

The name of John J. R. Macleod was well known to Banting. The professor was one of Canada's most distinguished medical scientists. His specialty was carbohydrate metabolism. It occurred to Banting that this procedure of his, so new and so foolproof, might be an old story to Macleod. He went to Toronto.

Dr. Macleod was unenthusiastic both about the idea and about Banting himself. Exactly what, the professor inquired, made Banting think that *he* could contribute anything to the study of pancreatic secretions? Did he know that the method he suggested had already been tried by renowned researchers in Europe? By pupils of Naunyn himself?

Banting admitted that he had not known exactly how much work had been done, but he hoped . . . Ah, Dr. Macleod interrupted, so Dr. Banting was not familiar with the literature on the subject? Well, for his information plenty of work had been done by the same method—but no one had ever succeeded.

Banting tried another approach. He was asking little, he told Macleod: just ten experimental animals, one assistant, a little laboratory space—and all for only eight weeks. After all, he reminded the professor, he *was* an alumnus of the university.

Macleod held out for several months. But to his surprise he was approached by quite a few influential people around the university who wanted to put in a good word for the shy young surgeon. Grudgingly the professor finally said that, since he was going to Scotland for the summer, part of the laboratory would be unused. If Banting wanted it for a short time, he could have it. That time, Macleod hinted, was just long enough for Banting to get the idea out of his head and get himself out of the laboratory.

Banting was delighted, but he still had a problem. He himself could handle all the surgery involved, but he was far from expert in chemistry. The whole project might fail because he was unable to take an accurate reading of a blood-sugar level, for example. Where could he find himself an assistant?

Macleod had a few students who were good at that sort of thing, he told Banting. They were young and therefore foolish, and they might enjoy puttering around the lab working on Banting's project.

One of these students was named Charles Best. He had majored in physiology and biochemistry and would get his A.B. degree in June. Although he usually spent his summers playing professional baseball to help meet the expenses of the coming year, he now joined in Banting's research. There was no salary involved. Banting could hardly pay his own room rent in Toronto.

The presence of Charles Best in the laboratory that summer was a rare piece of luck, as Banting would realize very shortly. The pre-medical student's skill in running off laboratory tests of which

Banting knew practically nothing was positively awesome.

In June, Banting resigned from the University of Western Ontario, sold his mortgaged house, and officially closed his practice. It was not much of a loss, he thought, as he drove his battered but well-beloved Ford into Toronto. He tried not to think about the folly of staking one's entire future on a borrowed laboratory and an idea.

Once he was installed in the laboratory, the first step was easy. Banting and Best anesthetized a few of their dogs and tied catgut ligatures around the ducts through which the strong digestive juices of the pancreas flow. Next came the wait of six to eight weeks, during which time the external cells of the organ were supposed to dry up. The two men spent the long weeks gathering and translating all the literature they could get their hands on. It was a blow to their morale. As he read more and more German journals, Banting realized that that this very same technique had indeed been tried before, as Macleod had said. And it had failed. No one had ever succeeded in isolating the internal secretion of the pancreas in a pure state. But the experiment had been tried by experts in the field, experienced scientists with money, equipment, trained assistants. It had, of course, never before been tried by an orthopedic surgeon and a college student, working without funds in a borrowed laboratory that had to be vacated in eight weeks.

Banting's frame of mind was in no way improved on the July day when he reopened the abdomens of the dogs. According to plan, the outer cells of the pancreas should now be dried up, leaving nothing but the islets of Langerhans. One dog after another was anesthetized, opened, and examined. One dog after another had as sound a pancreas as on the day of the original operation. Banting found that the ligatures were still present but had been walled off in a sort of bulb-shaped sac. A new canal had been formed in the duct itself. Gangrene under the ligature was responsible, and the gangrene, he realized, had developed because he had tied the ligatures too tightly. Yet he knew that, if the ligatures were tied too loosely, the ducts would also remain unblocked. He and Best would have to re-operate on all the dogs and tie off the ducts at exactly the right tension.

There was one problem. Although his patience was not yet exhausted, his cash was. It was indeed a gloom-filled day on which the Ford car, his last possession and one of the few joys of his life, was sold. With the meager proceeds, the two men paid room rent and bought new supplies.

The second ligaturing operations, performed with the most exquisite care, were undertaken early in

July. On the thirtieth of the month, barely four
weeks later, Banting decided to have a look at one
of the ligated pancreases. The two young men anesthetized a dog and removed the organ. This
time, they saw with relief, the ligatures had held

perfectly. The outer cells were shriveled up and had apparently lost all powers of secretion.

Within a few days, the dog, his pancreas completely removed, was showing all the symptoms of diabetes. Soon he began to sink into the coma characteristic of diabetes. Samples of his blood were found to be filled with sugar, far above the normal level.

Quickly the two men operated on a second dog. The surgeon removed the pancreas. The chemist cut the organ into tiny pieces, ground it up, then extracted the life-saving liquid from the inner cells by dissolving it in a chloride solution. The net result was a liquid which, if their calculations were correct, contained the pure secretion of the islets of Langerhans. Banting filled his syringe with the extract and then injected it into the veins of the dog that was dying of diabetes. Two hours later the dog was stirring. Three hours later he was fully conscious. He had come out of the diabetic coma, the unconscious state which had always been a death warrant. Laboratory tests now showed that the blood-sugar level was dropping to normal.

Later the two men realized how lucky their impatience had been. If they had waited much longer before preparing the extract from the ligated pancreas of the second dog, their experiments would have ended in failure, as earlier experiments on this method had done. The delicate secretion of the inner cells would have been destroyed.

The brilliant success of this first attempt alarmed the two men almost as much as failure would have disappointed them. It was much too good to be true. Before they could even think of telling anyone on the outside what had happened, they must have more to show than one live dog without a pancreas.

Neither of them had ever worked so hard before. Their friends knew that, at any given hour out of the twenty-four, either or both could always be found in the laboratory. Eating three meals a day was the first time-consuming habit to go. Most of their food was of the sort that could be brought in and heated over a Bunsen burner. During those hectic, happy days, on which Banting would soon look back with nostalgia, they began to unravel the secrets of the mysterious substance, or hormone. They called it "isletin."

Their greatest problem was the difficulty of keeping a supply of isletin on hand. Eight days after his restoration to life, their favorite dog had sunk back into a coma and died. The isletin, which had cost the life of several other dogs, had finally run out.

Banting and Best were greatly disturbed by the fact that so many dogs had to die in order to keep

one dog alive. They decided to turn all their energies to the search for a more plentiful source of
the life-saving liquid.

The logical solution was the use of larger animals. The logical place to find them was in the local
meat-packing house. After a series of long, hard
experiments, the two men worked out a method of
obtaining the product from the pancreases of slaugh-
tered cows. With this supply at their disposal, they
began to collect facts and figures. They learned the
exact amount of isletin needed to bring the greatest comfort to their canine patients. They learned
that an overdose of the marvelous stuff produced
its own set of symptoms, by lowering the blood-
sugar level too far. They worked out a special diet
to accompany the injections. Within a few weeks,
they had a notebook full of statistics complete
enough to convince a professional skeptic.

And they soon had one to convince.

Professor John J. R. Macleod was back in town.
He had stayed away longer than eight weeks. It
came as a shock, upon entering his own laboratory,
to be pawed over by a whirling mass of dogs and
to be told by the obnoxious young surgeon that
several of these happy animals had been living for
weeks without pancreases!

But Professor Macleod could hardly order Banting out of the building—not after he saw the rec-

ords the two men showed him. Macleod was a scientist, and his personal antagonism toward Banting could not prevent his appreciation of Banting's work. After some weeks of delay—agonizing delay to Banting and Best—the professor finally concluded that isletin was quite a discovery. His only objection to the stuff, in fact, was its name. For Dr. Banting's information, he announced, the secretion of islets of Langerhans had already been named, even though it had never before been isolated. Its name was "insulin."

Once converted, Macleod began to expedite the work. His own time and that of his many assistants was completely given over to the new research. The tedious job of purifying and standardizing the product was largely the work of a brilliant biochemist named James B. Collip. By January 11, 1922, insulin was ready for its first trial on a human being.

The patient was a 14-year-old boy in the last stages of diabetes. He was expected to die within the week. As Banting looked at the pale face of the boy, he knew that the lives of many children hung on the events of the next few hours.

The boy was given insulin in gradually increasing doses. Each injection was followed by a complete set of tests. In the laboratory one could read reports showing that each injection of insulin had resulted in a sharp drop of the blood-sugar level. In the sickroom, one could watch the boy's incredible restoration to life.

A child in a diabetic coma who was not going to die of diabetes? The disease had been known for four thousand years. What happened in the Toronto General Hospital in January of 1922 was happening for the first time.

One day in February a man named Joseph Gilchrist came to the laboratory. Banting had known Dr. Gilchrist for years. His weakened condition would have come as a shock if Banting had not known that his friend was suffering from diabetes. All diabetics eventually looked that way. Dr. Gilchrist's diabetes had reached a stage in which the most rigid diet no longer helped him. He was a doctor and a realist. He knew that he was near death.

"I hear something fancy is going on around here," he said to Banting. "I was wondering whether you needed a new rabbit."

"A rabbit?"

"A human rabbit," Dr. Gilchrist said.

Banting smiled slowly. "The job is yours," he said. "It starts now." He filled a syringe and gave his friend an immediate dose of insulin.

From that day on, Dr. Gilchrist was indeed the Number 1 rabbit of the laboratory. "There is probably not a person alive," Banting wrote later, "who has had more samples of blood taken from his veins." Every question the experimenters asked themselves about the proper use of insulin was answered in Dr. Gilchrist's body. On the basis of his good-natured, scientific descriptions of his reaction to various insulin experiments, a new chapter in medicine was being written.

In the middle of that year, the newspapers got

wind of the experiments in Toronto. Overnight, life became a nightmare for the reserved Banting. He had yet to learn the technique of dodging interviews. Nor did he have the knack of getting along with newsmen while not actually telling them anything. ("Banting Pearls Not for Swine," complained a headline, after a later attempt to interview the discoverer of insulin.)

The worst thing about the ill-timed publicity was the fact that premature hope had arisen all over the world. Banting was deluged with letters from people begging for insulin, pleading for permission to come to Toronto for treatment. His daily mail brought him evidence of more human misery than he had ever seen at close quarters. But there was nothing he could do for these desperate people. So far there was barely enough insulin available to keep the experimental patients alive. Not until 1923 did the supply even begin to meet the demand.

The succession of honorary degrees, citations, decorations, and titles that came to Banting was crowned in 1923 by the Nobel prize in medicine. Banting was naturally pleased that his work had been given the highest honor of all, but the award was not an unmixed joy. The prize committee had awarded the honor to two discoverers of insulin, and had split the prize money. But the co-discoverer cited was John J. R. Macleod. Banting, furious that Best had been neglected in favor of Macleod, immediately announced his intention of splitting his share of the prize with his associate.

The coolness between Banting and Macleod persisted to the end. In 1928 Macleod returned to Scotland, where he continued his own brilliant studies on the physiology of diabetes. His eventual successor as professor of physiology at the University of Toronto was Charles Best. Somewhere in the midst of his work on large-scale production methods for insulin, he had found time to pick up an M.D. degree. He had already qualified as the most illustrious pre-medical student in history.

In 1923 the University of Toronto inaugurated a new department called the Banting and Best Department of Medical Research. Banting, who only three years before had begged for the use of one laboratory and ten dogs, was appointed its head. "Surely," he wrote to Best, "blessings are falling on us fast enough now. We must keep our heads." They did, but one wonders how.

As chief of the new department, Banting undertook valuable research on cancer and on silicosis, one of Canada's most dangerous industrial diseases. During World War II, he turned his attention to designing a flying suit that would prevent the dreaded "blackout" among pilots. On his way to

England to help test this equipment, he was killed in an airplane crash.

Insulin occupies an almost unique position in the history of medicine. It has eliminated the word "hopeless" from descriptions of a disease for which a cure is unknown. It has given years of active, normal life to millions of people who would otherwise have been doomed to an early and miserable death. They have good reason to be glad that a young physiology professor once believed in doing extra homework.

10

ALEXANDER FLEMING

---------- 1881 – 1955 ----------

The Discovery
of Penicillin

The fall of 1928 was damp, outstandingly damp even for London. The basement laboratory of St. Mary's Hospital was ventilated by one slightly open window through which drifted leaves, dust, and other wind-blown particles calculated to annoy a research scientist.

Dr. Alexander Fleming, the hospital's bacteriologist, was writing an article on the behavior of staphylococci. These are tough little bacilli responsible for a variety of ailments from boils to blood poisoning.

A friend had dropped by the lab for a visit. As the two men chatted, Dr. Fleming occupied himself by washing out some culture plates that had been contaminated by airborne molds. Fine cultures

of staphylococci were constantly being ruined by molds. Since Dr. Fleming was Scotch by birth and serene by nature, such accidents did not bother him. They were inevitable. He took one of the plates over to the sink and turned the faucet. As he did so he glanced casually at the plate, blinked, and then shut off the water.

"That's funny—" he said, holding out the plate to his friend.

The culture plate was indeed a curious sight. On its outer edges the colonies of bacteria were still flourishing. But in the area immediately surrounding the mold, the staphylococci had disappeared.

"If my mind had not been in a reasonably perceptive state, I would not have paid any attention to it," Fleming wrote later, recalling this wonderful day. "I might have been in a bad temper, say, after a quarrel with my wife; I might have just become engaged and my mind might have been full of the young woman, or I might have been suffering from the after-effects of too heavy a meal and been mentally too sluggish to notice it." But he had noticed it. And, "instead of casting out the contaminated mold with appropriate language," he investigated.

The mold which had floated in the window was identified as a species of the genus Penicillium.

The substance it secreted, which killed the staphylococci, the doctor named "penicillin." By simmering a community of mold, grown from his original stray, in a broth for two weeks, Dr. Fleming produced a small quantity of this fluid. Then he began to make it perform.

For years Alexander Fleming had been looking for a substance capable of killing off deadly bacteria. During World War I, he had found how useless against infection and how dangerous to the tissues were the strong chemicals that were then the only defense against invading microbes. He had already discovered—in human tears—a mysterious substance called lysozyme, which showed remarkable powers against hostile bacteria. He knew as much about the subject as any man alive. Yet nothing in his long experience could begin to equal the performance of this stray mold that had floated in through his window and planted itself on his culture plate.

Staphylococci, he soon found, were not the only members of the microbe world that penicillin attacked. In dilutions of one part to six hundred, it could also prevent the growth of streptococci and pneumococci, two of the most common man-killers. Even the tough bacilli of diphtheria succumbed to it. But the microbe least affected by the broth was the weak, pallid creature that causes influenza. Obviously penicillin did not work according to any set of rules yet made.

Was it dangerous? That of course was the big question. Lots of chemical antiseptics also killed bacteria in a test tube. But the body could not tolerate them. Dr. Fleming took two healthy rabbits. Into one he injected twenty cubic centimeters of penicillin broth, and into the other twenty cubic centimeters of ordinary broth. He found that penicillin was not toxic—at least to rabbits.

The problem he now faced would be the plague of penicillin researchers for the next fourteen years. His supply of the mold was tiny. He consulted a biologist named Dr. Harold Raistrick. Together the two friends began an intensive campaign to grow penicillin. When they had on hand a small, jealously guarded store of it, they were ready to tackle the biggest question of all. Penicillin killed microbes in a test tube. Would it do the same to microbes in the human body?

"We tried a little in clinical work," Fleming says, "but not much. We tried it tentatively on a few old sinuses . . . and though the reports were favorable there was nothing miraculous. When we went to the wards and asked the surgeons if they had any septic cases we could try it on, they always said, like most surgeons in most places, I think, that they had none."

In one way the cautious surgeons were right, for Fleming made no secret of the fact that he had barely enough of the stuff to treat one case. "We were bacteriologists, not chemists, and in view of the difficulties the chemists have had in concentrating penicillin, it is not surprising that our amateur efforts at concentration were not successful."

But if they could interest biologists and mold experts in penicillin, Fleming thought, then someone, somewhere, might come up with a solution to the problem of production. He wrote a report on his laboratory experiments and presented it at a medical meeting. In the crush of other papers, on less tenuous subjects than floating molds, the report was quietly overlooked.

The years passed. In St. Mary's laboratory, penicillin was used as a quick way to distinguish between certain types of bacteria because of its indifference to some and its violent antagonism to others. For ten years Alexander Fleming kept a small strain of it in a corner of the lab and a vast love for it in his heart.

In 1935 the production of the sulfa drugs caused a great stir in the world of medicine, and—as often happens—overdramatic claims were made about the power of these valuable chemicals. Years later a friend recalled a luncheon conversation on the subject with Fleming.

"You know, Mac," Fleming said, "I have something much better—but no one will listen to me. I can't get anyone to be interested in it, nor a chemist who will extract it for me."

"What's the name of it?"

"I named it penicillin."

"I've never heard of it."

Few people outside Fleming's laboratory ever had.

But in Oxford two biochemists named Florey and Chain were doing research on "bacterial antagonisms." They ploughed through hundreds of back issues of medical magazines and finally came up with articles about three "antagonistic" substances that seemed promising. One of the three articles was Fleming's original paper on penicillin.

The two men went into conference in their favorite consultation room—a bench under the huge elm tree near the laboratory. They decided that, of the three substances, Fleming's mold broth had the greatest possibilities.

This was in 1937. By the next year it had become abundantly clear that England, and perhaps the whole world, would soon be at war. Before long, hospitals might be overflowing with wounded men. Of all the problems that war would present to medical researchers, none was more important than a way to check infection.

Florey and Chain soon realized that Alexander Fleming had not exaggerated in his report on penicillin. A young chemist named Heatley joined the team. After the usual irritating resistance from the Penicillium mold, the three men finally succeeded in obtaining a higher concentration of penicillin than had yet been possible. From this they produced the first penicillin salt.

In 1940, with England already under heavy attack, they made their first decisive experiment. Florey shot 50 mice full of the deadliest strain of streptococci he could get his hands on. He left 25 untreated. The other 25 were given shots of penicillin at three-hour intervals for forty-five hours. Of the untreated mice, all 25 died within sixteen hours. Of the penicillin-treated mice, 24 out of the 25 lived.

These sensational results were published on August 24, 1940, in *The Lancet*. Alexander Fleming, like most doctors in England, glanced through each issue of the weekly medical journal to see what was new and interesting. It is hard even to imagine the emotions he felt while reading the report from Oxford.

Within a short time he was knocking on the

door of Florey's and Chain's laboratory. He was Alexander Fleming, he explained to the astonished scientists, and he had come to see what penicillin looked like in a pure state. The two men were barely able to speak. They had somehow assumed that Alexander Fleming was dead.

Fleming sent Florey a strain of the Penicillium mold descended from his original colony. The Oxford men now began preparing a supply for their first tests of penicillin on human beings. Yet Florey began the experiments with a heavy heart. For there was an unfortunate problem with the magical substance. The Oxford men had realized it from their very first animal experiments. The body does not retain penicillin. It is thrown out almost as quickly as it can be forced in—"like pouring water down a basin with the plug out," Florey said. The amount necessary to keep 25 mice alive had almost used up the laboratory supply. Could they now produce an amount large enough to treat one man? What, for that matter, did they hope to prove by being able to treat one man, when men in that year were dying by the thousands and being wounded by the tens of thousands?

In February of 1941, a London policeman cut his face while shaving. It was a common enough accident, but, as it developed in this case, a terrible one. Two weeks later the man was dying, his body invaded by a horde of staphylococci against which the sulfa preparations had no effect.

The case was made to order for the purposes of Florey and his associates. Every available bit of penicillin in the laboratory was taken to the Radcliffe Infirmary of Oxford. The dying man was given a dose of penicillin injected directly into the blood stream every three hours. Five days passed— or crawled, as it seemed to Florey. Within two days a slight drop in temperature was noted; on the third day the horrible swellings on the policeman's face began to subside. The next day his temperature was almost normal, and by the fifth day his recovery seemed assured. But by the fifth day the last fleck of penicillin was gone.

In the laboratory, heartbreaking efforts were made to scrape some more together. The efforts came too late. Before the treatment could be resumed, the infection again flared up. The policeman died.

By some standards the first trial of penicillin had failed, since the patient was dead. Actually those who had followed the case were now more convinced than ever of the drug's effectiveness. They worked feverishly to cultivate a new batch.

In the Oxford laboratory, the telephone rang early one morning. "Florey? Fletcher here. I have a case that I think you might want to look at. Fifteen-year-old boy. Hemolytic strep infection. Sulfas can't do a thing for it. I don't give him another forty-eight hours to live. Unless—"

That time it happened. The boy who should have been dead within forty-eight hours, by all existing standards, stayed alive. Once again the supply of penicillin was exhausted, but this time it had held out just long enough. "Now," Florey thought grimly, "we have to have more of the stuff."

It was a vicious circle. Penicillin research had reached the point at which it demanded large-scale experiments in clinics all over the world. So far, enough penicillin had been produced to treat two patients, one unsuccessfully. Unless the drug were manufactured by the ton, not the teaspoon, widespread experiments would never be made. Yet no drug manufacturer would say, "Certainly, Doctor, I'll be glad to spend a few millions to set up production of this unknown drug which has failed in 50 per cent of the two cases you've tried it on." No, Florey reasoned, he had to have more figures —figures that would appeal to the sales manager of a drug company as well as to its laboratory director.

He enlisted the services of his wife, Ethel, a physician who thought she had retired from any practice more active than taking care of the two Florey children. While he and his associates devoted their full energies to squeezing every fraction of a milligram that could be squeezed from the temperamental mold, Dr. Ethel Florey took charge of the clinical research. By the end of the following year, Florey had 187 carefully documented cases of penicillin therapy. They included cases of osteomyelitis, streptococcus meningitis, bacterial endocarditis, empyema, and septicemia.

In the meantime they looked for a way to put penicillin into production on a larger scale. England was too busy with the desperate necessities of war to take on a new, untried industry. The drug would have to be produced elsewhere.

In 1941 Howard Florey and Norman Heatley were brought to the United States by the Rockefeller Foundation. They carried with them a sample of the mold descended from Alexander Fleming's original airborne visitor.

Florey and Heatley were hustled onto a train and taken to Peoria, Illinois. There the scientists of the Fermentation Division of the Northern Regional Research Laboratory faced up to the problem at once. "Either we find some new way to grow this stuff, or we forget all about it." They began to look for a better medium in which to raise it.

One day, while Dr. A. J. Moyer was making a routine check of his flasks, he found that one of them was producing two hundred units of penicillin to every cubic centimeter—200,000 to a liter instead of the 1,000 to a liter that had been produced in the Oxford laboratory. What was the experimental medium that had so intoxicating an effect on the mold? Simple, home-brewed, Peoria corn-steep liquor.

The bottleneck was broken. With production up two hundred times almost overnight, drug manufacturers who had said, "Sorry, not interested," were now eager to talk business. All over the United States, chemists, bacteriologists, engineers, government officials, military officials, and medical research men were sitting up late over their notebooks and their test tubes.

The cooperative venture paid off in units of penicillin. During the first five months of commercial production, 400,000,000 units of the severely rationed product were turned out. By the end of the year the figure had jumped to 9,194,000,000 units a month. From then on the figures became astronomical.

A great new field of research now opened. If nature had concealed so powerful a weapon in a humble airborne mold, then surely she had tucked away others in unlikely places. An imposing list of antibiotics—the name given to a living organism that has the power to kill bacteria—joined penicillin: aureomycin, chloromycetin, terramycin, neomycin, polymyxin, and many others. In 1943 Dr. Selman Waksman discovered streptomycin in the throat of a chicken. It was the first antibiotic to give real, substantial promise in the fight against tuberculosis.

Sir Alexander Fleming—knighthood was only one of the many honors that came to him—wrote: "There are thousands of different molds and there are thousands of different bacteria, and that chance put that mold in the right spot at the right time was like winning the Irish sweepstakes."

He should have added that there are also thousands of bacteriologists. Very likely other Penicillium molds had settled on other culture plates in other laboratories—and had been thrown down the drain. "In the field of observation," Louis Pasteur once said, "chance helps the mind that is prepared." It was one of the happiest accidents in history—if such things are really accidents—that sent the mold along to spoil a culture belonging to Alexander Fleming.

11

CONCLUSION

Medical Research
and the Future

Thousands of years ago, our cave-dwelling ancestors believed that the only way to cure a sick person was to pacify or bribe whatever evil spirit or dead relative was holding a grudge.

A few hundred years ago, our colony-founding ancestors believed that the best way to cure a sick person was to let as much blood out of him as possible, in order to release the disease from his body.

In the light of our present knowledge it is easy to look over the errors of the past and think: How could people have been so stupid? Couldn't they see the truth? It's so obvious.

The truth is always obvious—after someone else has figured it out.

Think how many people had to figure things out in order to bring us to our present point of knowledge about medicine. The road leading to this point has been long and often dark, full of detours and full of paths that seemed promising, yet in the end turned out to be dead ends. But scattered along the way there have always been landmarks. They came in the shape of widely different discoveries. Some of them seemed so small that it was hardly thought necessary to record them. Others were world-shaking. Some appeared in a blinding flash of intuition and formed a part of our scientific heritage almost at once. Still others were laboriously put together like jigsaw puzzles, each piece being added over a period of years until at the end only one fragment was needed to make the picture complete.

How many great names there are in the history of medicine! The ten we have met in this book are only a small fraction of them. We have had to by-pass men without whose genius and vision medicine as we know it today would not exist. Men like Boerhaave, who first introduced the medical student to the patient. Haller, the founder of modern physiology. Morgagni and Baillie, who gave a system to pathology. The brilliant, feuding Hunter brothers, John and William, to whom surgery and obstetrics are greatly indebted. Virchow, who first saw the human body as a "cell state in which every cell is a citizen." Wunderlich, who began to take the patient's temperature and write it on a chart. Or men like Lind and Eijkman and Hopkins and Funk and Goldberger, and the others who taught us about food . . .

Think, too, what debts the doctors owe to their fellow scientists. We have seen the greatest example in Louis Pasteur, the chemist who caused a medical revolution. There were other chemists, Priestley and Lavoisier, on whose work depends our knowledge of the very breath of life. There were physicists, Wilhelm Röntgen and Marie Curie, who gave doctors two of their mightiest weapons, the X-ray and radium.

Only about a hundred years have passed since Louis Pasteur went to work in Paris, in an attic laboratory so cold that his crystals often froze in their test tubes. Think how medical knowledge has changed in those relatively few years. Our modern laboratories, our great foundations with their heavy financial backing for medical research, the intensive training of our students in medicine and science, the public attitude of respect and, indeed, of positive awe toward the scientist—all these things would have amazed the hopeful young professor from Arbois.

The bitter resistance to progress and change and

new ideas that plagued so many of the early heroes of medicine has broken down. We cannot say it no longer exists, but it is certainly the exception where it was once the rule.

The germ theory of disease laid out the work of a hundred years in medical research. There is nothing in human history that can be compared with the success of that work. The pattern of work for the coming years is already clear: cancer research, endocrinology, study of the heart and blood vessels. With the current appreciation of medical research, the future of this work seems bright.

Let us hope that the coming generation of medical researchers will attack as enthusiastically the haunting specter of mental disease, which looms ahead as the greatest medical problem left to be solved. In this area both our knowledge and our attitudes lag painfully behind.

Alexander Fleming once remarked that penicillin could not have been discovered in a great modern laboratory. Nothing as primitive as an open window and a stray particle of mold would be permitted nowadays in a roomful of culture plates.

He did not, of course, mean that laboratories *should* have impurities floating about. Perhaps what he had in mind was the fact that great new discoveries in medicine will not be made just because of wonderful laboratories, or new equipment, or computing machines, or work-saving methods of team research. All these are contributing factors. The essential need remains the same as it was in the days of Fleming or Pasteur or Laennec or Jenner or Vesalius—the individual spark of genius in the mind of the solitary thinker.

Author's Note

The books listed in the Bibliography are only a few of the works that were consulted in the preparation of *Great Men of Medicine*, both in its original edition and its new version as a World Landmark book. I have tried to uncover every source of information about these ten men, in order to make these accounts as accurate and factual as possible.

The word "factual" raises the question of the conversations used in this book. In writing biography, three kinds of dialogue are possible. The first is the use of words actually spoken by the subject and recorded either by himself or by an ear-witness. The more recently a man lived, the more likely we are to have examples of this. All the quotations from Sir Alexander Fleming, for example, are actual conversations. So is the dialogue in the chapter on Morton, because the years of lawsuits and Congressional hearings over the discovery of anesthesia produced volumes of reminiscences and testimony.

The second kind of dialogue is this: if we know that a certain conversation took place, or that a man once expressed such and such an opinion, then we can reconstruct the words he might have used. In Chapter 1 of this book, the classroom comments of Sylvius and the conversation between Vesalius and his friends are examples of this kind. So is the scene between the milkmaid and Dr. Ludlow in Chapter 3, and the famous argument between Laënnec and Broussais in Chapter 4. All these conversations actually took place, but I have had to guess at the exact words that were spoken.

The third type of dialogue is that used in conversations that are entirely imaginary and are made up in order to convey information in an interesting way. There is only one example of this in the book: the talk between Paré and the two surgeons around the campfire. From his writings we know all of Paré's views on the subject and the fact that he used to argue about his methods with his colleagues.

I am grateful to the E. P. Dutton Company for permission to use material from André Maurois' recent life of Sir Alexander Fleming. It is a fascinating biography which I recommend to readers of this book. I would also like to express my admiration and appreciation of the work of Dr. J. B. Saunders and Dr. Charles D. O'Malley on Andreas Vesalius. It is one of the great pieces of scholarship of our time, and all students of the history of medicine are deeply in their debt.

I am greatly indebted to Dr. Thomas R. Forbes, of the Yale University School of Medicine, for helpful suggestions about this book. Lastly my thanks go to the wonderfully informed, generous, and friendly staff of the National Library of Medicine, Washington, D. C.

Bibliography

Ball, James M., *Andreas Vesalius, the Reformer of Anatomy* (1910)

Baron, John, *Life of Edward Jenner* (1827)

Compton, Piers, *The Genius of Louis Pasteur* (1932)

Drewitt, F., *The Life of Edward Jenner* (1933)

Füllop-Miller, René, *Triumph Over Pain* (1938)

Godlee, Sir Rickman, *Lord Lister* (revised edition 1924)

Harris, Seale, *Banting's Miracle: The Story of the Discovery of Insulin* (1946)

La Grange, Emile, *Robert Koch, Sa Vie et Ses Oeuvres* (1938)

Ludovici, Laurence J., *Fleming: Discoverer of Penicillin* (1952)

Maurois, André, *The Life of Sir Alexander Fleming* (1959)

Metchnikoff, Elie, *The Founders of Modern Medicine* (1939)

Morton, W. T. G., *Statements Supported by Evidence . . . on Claims to the Discovery of the Anaesthetic Properties of Ether* (1853)

Packard, Francis, *The Life and Times of Ambroise Paré* (1921)

Rice, Nathan, *Trials of a Public Benefactor* (1859 ; written in part by Morton)

Saunders, J. B., and O'Malley, Charles D., *The Illustrations from the Works of Andreas Vesalius of Brussels* (1950)

Sigerist, Henry, *The Great Doctors* (1933)

Vallery-Radot, René, *The Life of Pasteur* (1919)

Walker, Kenneth, *Joseph Lister* (1956)

Webb, Gerald, *René Théophile Hyacinthe Laënnec* (1928)

Index